How To Grow Old
Without Aging

By
Rev. Andrew D. Phillips

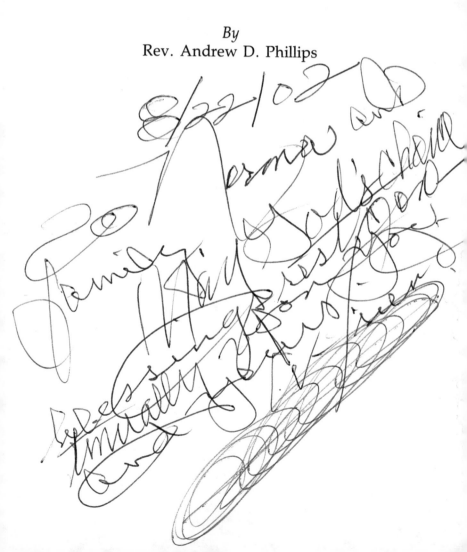

How To Grow Old Without Aging

By
Rev. Andrew D. Phillips

VINCOM, Inc.
Tulsa, Oklahoma

How To Grow Old Without Aging
ISBN No. 0-927936-30-5.
Copyright © 1992 by Rev. Andrew D. Phillips
1439 North Frankfort
Tulsa, OK 74106

Published by
VINCOM, Inc.
P. O. Box 702400
Tulsa, OK 74170

Contents

The Author Speaks

Inspiration for the writing of this book came to me from four distinct sources. I am deeply grateful to each source for the part they played.

First, the churches I have pastored in Texas and Oklahoma during my ministerial career have inspired me to write this book. These churches have served as the mills from which I have derived the grist of inspiration, encouragement and determination. They tolerated my errors and shortcomings and profited by their own, just as I have. They furnished the mixture of the thistle and the balm, both essential to complete self-orientation and preparation.

In these churches, I observed people and had the pleasure and blessing of having them help me do God's work through their role as witnesses for Christ.

The witness to the Word, consecration to the cause and selflessness of the people have been the "fuel in flight" and the "lift" I needed to "mount up with wings as eagles" in preaching the Gospel.

Secondly, my special inspiration has been given by my devoted and untiring wife, Bernice, and my sons, Phil, David and Danny. These have been my "thrust" toward tirelessness and my "boost" toward excellence.

It is they who have helped me "run" and not be weary in strength and to walk and not faint in spirit.

Thirdly, my appreciation goes to my church members at The Greater Mount Rose Baptist Church, Tulsa, Oklahoma.

Fourthly, I wish to acknowledge the numerous ministers and friends across the country who have been an immense source of inspiration, challenge and courage. Among these are the Rev. David Hill, Pastor, New Hope Baptist Church, Amarillo, Texas, and Rev. Jim Rowe, Pastor, Solid Rock Baptist Church, Tulsa, Oklahoma.

It is with all of these precious people and leaders that I have fallen into the ground of the Gospel ministry and died so I could bring forth much Gospel fruit!

Rev. Andrew D. Phillips

Purpose

Many people of this age grow old, inactive and a burden to society prematurely and unnecessarily, victims of the "go-ahead-and-get-old, it's your time" syndrome.

Usually, whenever a person reaches the seasoned time of life, the general sentiment is that it is time for them to stop driving, stop traveling and stop being president or whatever professional or non-professional service they are rendering. While many, for various reasons, need to discontinue these activities, others become wanton wastes, for many of these persons enter their season of sobriety when they could be of maximum service and use to society and humanity.

It is the purpose of this book to call attention to this waste of time, talent, expertise and usefulness and to suggest practices, programs and principles which are advisable and available.

More emphasis is given to what to do after a person becomes old instead of what progressive and preventable measures may be employed to minimize, arrest and delay the maladies and debilitating disabilities before these evil days come.

The foremost antagonist to the positive progression of older persons is the lack of systematic, continuous and consistent exercise. Many of the disabilities, diseases and disadvantages of older people could be postponed or, in some cases avoided, through a program of moral and body-building exercises.

This regime of recreational exercise will not only improve the health and general physical conditions, but will:

1. Increase and preserve the mental and spiritual competence as well.

2. Reserve a productive and supporting member of the family for a longer period of time.

3. Reduce the health cost factor of the home, permitting saved monies to be used to greater advantage.

It is to these and other positive ends that this book is written. It is written with the hope and prayer that individuals, churches, communities and the national government will re-think the matter of aging to the point that its fear, repugnance and abhorrence will be turned to a state of hope, happiness and wholeness.

Shalom!

Foreword

I first met Andrew Phillips in 1962 and for the past thirty years, I have, with great pleasure, watched Andrew interact with life in a consistently optimistic and forward-thinking fashion. He has been active and involved with many issues, always timely and always with the mind of a young man seeking to be in tune with his times.

Physically, he has rarely had significant medical problems, and the only concerns have been ones that have interfered temporarily with his love of life. In recent years, he has become very active physically, attaining remarkable achievements in a very young man's sport (karate), and he has on several occasions visited me because of the kinds of bruises and soft tissue injuries that I usually see in men fifty years younger.

He has been a leader in showcasing the rights of minorities and has used his position as a Christian minister wisely and carefully in this regard. I am now pleased to see him using his own experiences and his own concern and care for the physical body in encouraging others to follow a healthy, active lifestyle.

I can think of no one better suited to that purpose, and I heartily endorse this fruit of the author's intellect and enthusiasm.

Richard A. Liebendorfer, M.D.

1
The Aging Process

The process of growing old has plagued mankind for years, and all efforts to diminish, delay, or deter its ravaging forces have failed.

From time immemorial, the fear of growing old has persisted. In modern times, countless efforts have been made to circumvent the aging process. From Ponce de Leon's fountain of youth to today's vitamins and minerals, hope has sprung eternal, soared and died, and the young continue to get old and the old get older.

Obviously, there is no way to compromise time, to diminish the dispersion of deterioration, or repress the process of growing older. However, there is an alternative. In this book, an approach to a better and longer life will be discussed.

You're As Old As You Think!

"For as he thinketh in his heart, so is he..." (Proverbs 23:7).

The psychological concession to the notion of growing old is that oldness comes by decision more than by years.

Between 50 and 60 years of age, many people, without provocation or coercion, begin to close themselves in. They remove themselves from recreational activities, sports and other community interests that tend to preserve youthful entities into the senior years.

The adage, "You're only as old as you think" is true. We are affected more by what we think than by what others think or say of us. To a great extent, our thoughts control our personalities, communication and conduct. Our attitude, mentality and health are greatly conditioned by what and how we think.

What Thoughts Should We Think?

Thoughts can be controlled in the same way eating, drinking and moral conduct are controlled: by discipline, perseverance, persistence, determination and hard work! Sour, evil and negative thoughts push themselves uninvitedly and unwantedly into the mind and inflict themselves upon the conscienceness.

Undesirable, unkind and unpleasant thoughts should be dealt with just as you would deal with a bad odor. You may be forced to breathe the smell, but you breathe in as little as possible, while exhaling as much as possible. With the ugly, destructive, unlovable thoughts that press themselves upon us and push their way into a decision-making process, we are forced to give them attention, but we don't have to give them *sanctuary*.

The harder you strive to cast off, reject and push unwanted thoughts from your mind, the more you will succeed.

In Matthew 12:43-45, we are told of an evil spirit leaving a man, but later re-entering him with seven additional wicked spirits because the empty space was not refilled with a better spirit. It is equally urgent then that thoughts of hatred, prejudice, racism, envy and injustice be forced out of our consciousness and be *replaced* with thoughts of love, patience, goodwill, hope and faith.

A person's age does not have as great an impact on them as *how* that person views and reacts to his age.

There are many factors which tend to neutralize or balance old age. One of them is *health of the body, mind and spirit.* The relationship of the body and spirit will be treated in other chapters, while we will look at the health of the mind in this chapter.

Health of the Mind

Just as the body thrives on good food, the mind thrives, grows and expands on good "thought" food. Just as you must be selective with natural food, you must be discriminating with "thought" food.

Just as the body needs rest and recreation, the mind needs "mind rest" in engagement, activities, endeavors and hobbies. The aging person should be enthusiastic about extracurricular activities of the type that rest the mind. Travel, sightseeing, movies, reading, fishing, window shopping and shopping are among the diversions that relax the mind.

The Apostle Paul admonished us on what we should think: **"Finally, brethren, whatsoever things are true, whatsoever things are honest, whatsoever things are just, whatsoever things are pure, whatsoever things are of good report; if there be any virtue, and if there be any praise, think on these things"** (Philippians 4:8).

Thoughts on truth tend to terminate tension and provide a wealth of strength. Thoughts on honesty hone the spirit of integrity and provide a haven of self-worth for the journey of life.

Thoughts on the lovely concepts of life lift the mind above lowlands of lethargy and raise the spiritual vision to the highlands of compassionate concern. **"As cold waters to a thirsty soul, so is good news from a far country"** (Proverbs 25:25). So says the wisdom of Solomon. The feeble, evil mind reveals garbage news, negative negotiations, rotten reports and condescending conversation. The mind of victorious virtue centers in on the aesthetics, the real and the wholesome.

Admittedly, it is difficult to think good thoughts of people who antagonize and persecute. Self-discipline and perseverance and help from God afford the power and the grace to triumph in such situations.

Although I did not acquire this discipline in earlier years, it has paid great social and spiritual dividends in my later years. It has given me the youth of years, the mentality of middle age and the physical energy of a younger athlete. It has prompted the comment from peers and other people I have known for years, "You look younger than you did 25 years ago."

It is also true that my general health today is better, I feel stronger and I can perform some feats I could not in earlier years.

Thinking good thoughts, even of your enemies, gives you the ability to go from strength to strength — and to enjoy the journey in the process!

2
Healthy Eating Habits

In this chapter, we will deal with the subject of "eating" as opposed to the subject of "diet."

Health authorities and dieticians agree that "food laws" should be followed during a person's younger years, but even more so in the later years.

The kind and quantity of food you should eat vary with health, size, weight and general body condition. However, I believe it is safe to assume that most people should eat a high percentage of vegetables, fruits, nuts, non-fat lean meat and low-calorie foods. These foods are essential to the health and longevity of a person's life, especially for the older person.

The following suggestions have been adapted from a Hillcrest Hospital, Tulsa, Oklahoma, publication called **"55 Plus Outlook"** and are highly recommended for older persons.

Practice Healthy Eating Habits

No one food gives you all of the nutrients you need, so eating different types of healthy foods is the best way to ensure proper nutrition.

* Eat high-fiber foods (bran cereals, whole wheat bread, fruit).

* Cut down on fats and sweets (a fruit salad instead of cake and ice cream; diet margarine instead of butter).

* Eat foods that are not over-processed (a baked potato instead of instant potatoes).

* Dine at home instead of eating out. (Restaurant meals tend to contain more fat, salt and calories than meals prepared at home.)

Exercise Regularly

Exercise helps maintain healthy weight and body composition (ratio of fat to muscle). Being overweight increases your risk of diabetes. Exercise and any extra movement burn calories and make weight control easier.

* Walk instead of driving short distances.

* Use the stairs instead of the elevator.

* Do slow stretching exercises to loosen your muscles.

Discipline Yourself in Eating

Many Americans eat too much. That's just a fact. The ''three meals a day - eat until you are full'' syndrome is not good for young people, and it certainly isn't good for older people. How much you eat should depend in part on your occupation, the kind of work you do and the calories that will be burned in work or other physical activity.

Since most older persons aren't in the heavy calorie-burning category, they should be extremely careful about overeating. One or two average- or small-sized meals a day with one or two snacks is far better for older people than two or three heavy meals.

I am an active person, more active, even athletically, than many men who are younger than I. My meal frequency on the average is two meals a day and perhaps a snack. I feel much better when I eat lightly. Sometimes I have one meal and two snacks. At other times, I have one meal and one snack, depending upon my activity schedule for the day. If I plan to do lots of walking, getting in and out of the car, jogging and other calorie-burning exercises, I eat more than on the days I sit at my desk.

Just enough of the right kinds of food to give the body the necessary energy to accomplish its workload for the day is better for the older person. Even a locomotive runs easier, faster and longer with a light load!

Most of us have heard that breakfast is the most important meal of the day. This is not necessarily true. Three factors affect the validity of this statement.

1. How late did you eat the night before? A person who gets off work at midnight and eats before going to bed may not need breakfast.

2. What did you eat and how much did you eat before you retired? If you have a light snack at 9:00 p.m. before retiring, you will likely be hungry at breakfast time. On the other hand, if you have a full meal before retiring at 9:00 or 10:00 p.m., you may not be hungry or need to eat at breakfast time.

3. What mode of activity is anticipated on a given day? If I am facing a day of unusual physical activity, I always eat a good breakfast. This gives me energy for the day's pull on my body. If I am anticipating a

quiet day at the office or I am sleeping late, I may not eat breakfast.

Eat Much Less, Live Longer!

An article published in the *Tulsa World* in 1990 said that evidence from animal studies suggested that the way to live longer — and reduce the danger of cancer — is to eat less, much less.

The article said that diet restriction extends longevity in nearly all species so far tested, according to Pathologist Richard Weindruch from the National Institute of Aging. He also said that the reduction in food intake required to have much effect may be severe. In animals, the food was cut by as much as 70 percent. It is not known whether such results apply to humans, because the studies have not been done with humans.

Weindruch also said, speaking at an American Cancer Society Seminar for science writers, that cutting food intake is, so far, the only thing that convincingly and always extends life span. He also emphasized the importance of not cutting too drastically on food intake.

Weindruch said that evidence supporting the idea of life extension by food restriction dates back as far as 1090. Numerous studies done since have supported this finding.

It is commonly believed that a person should not eat late at night. Again, it depends on the time, the person and the condition. Our bodies are not identical in their biological structure or in their functional needs. One person can eat any hour of the night and have no physical reaction and the body may thrive on the practice, while another may have an adverse reaction with the slightest amount eaten late at night.

Individually, older people must determine for themselves which group they fit into.

All of my adult life, I have eaten late at night. I have, however, practiced some discretion. I concern myself with what I eat, how much I eat and I give some time for digestion before retiring. People, like myself, who do much of their work during late night hours, do well, if not better, without breakfast. I rarely eat breakfast, and I seem to work and feel better as a result.

While I have experienced no apparent negative effects from this practice, it has been my experience that the best sleep usually comes with little or no food consumption at bed time.

It is perhaps better to avoid late-night eating. Human nature varies so drastically from one person to another — even in the physical makeup — that one set of health rules isn't necessarily good for everyone. People vary as much in their physiological makeup as in their mental, emotional and spiritual makeup. Each person must discover what works best for him/her.

Generous amounts and a variety of fresh vegetables should be included in the older person's diet. The two stages of life when vegetables are most needed are in childhood and in older life.

In the older person's life, fresh vegetables tend to regulate bowel activity, preventing constipation and resultant headaches, stomach upset and other disorders. Many of the digestive minerals, vitamins and other dietary supplements needed for nourishment of the body, especially for the older body, are found in vegetables.

Fruits, nuts, lean meats, cereals and other health foods are ''musts'' for the aging person. Sweets, starches, fats and highly-spiced foods are among the foods that should be avoided. In order to maximize the digestion and usefulness of food, it must be eaten slowly and chewed well. The meal should be eaten in a quiet, pleasant atmosphere.

It is also unadvisable to have an extended conversation during meal time where the older person does most of the talking. Talking while eating causes the ingestion of a great amount of air, which can result in digestive and respiratory problems.

While it is enjoyable to have guests or share a meal in the company of others, it is also important that an older person have quiet, meditative meals in the tranquility and silence of a table or booth to themselves.

I enjoy sharing sessions around the dining table with my family and others. Frequently, however, I take refuge in the quietness and solitude of a table or booth to myself. Reading is good company while you eat if you are alone. It gives opportunity to:

1. Nourish the body with the needed food for health and energy.

2. Catch up on reading.

3. Maximize meditation.

Some of the most enjoyable times are those spent with food over a newspaper and/or a good book.

An older person should always remember that the body of a person who does little or no exercise does not need a great amount of food. Three meals a day may not be needed for such a person.

The stomach does not have to be full to be happy. In reality, the stomach is happier when half full rather than when completely full.

Older people should avoid the ''all you can eat'' bargains. In these situations, the psychological temptation to stuff is overwhelming. Don't be driven by the ''I'm paying for it — I might as well eat it'' syndrome!

The old adage, ''Eat to live, don't live to eat'' is still a good watchword for the older person.

3

Avoid a "Hurry-Scurry" Pace

Anxiety is the offspring of insecurity, and the two give the false impression that there frequently comes a need to rush.

These pressures are unhealthy, even for the young, but are particularly damaging to older people. It is a false notion that rushing makes up for lost time or that it will prevent failure.

The temptation to rush is strong, because progressively, the feeling persists that a person must keep up, complete, hold on, be a part of and succeed.

It is urgent to consider that the body's reaction to stimuli slows down with age. The body cannot respond as it did in younger years.

To attempt to force the same degree of response in later years will result in unprofitable strain, unnecessary stress and undesirable damage to the body and to the mind.

The older person must resist the temptation to get caught up in today's "hurry up, rush about" society. On the surface, rushing appears to be a need. However, it is more of a practice which grows into a habit, becoming a way of life.

The "exterminator anxiety" with its accomplice, "killer stress," lay in wait to ambush the careless and unsuspecting older person who gets caught up in the "rush order."

It takes a measure of boldness and strong reliance on the Supreme Being to be able to be about one's tasks, duties and responsibilities with unhurried dispatch.

This kind of boldness and belief breeds self-confidence, and a great degree of self-confidence is imperative if a person is to move into the areas of responsibility, demand, challenge and uncertainty with positiveness. This confidence par excellence, unlike most other strengths, comes from without; not, however, from the immediate outside, but from the realm of the Strong, the Source of all sources, the Supplier of all systems and the Providential Provider for all people — God.

With this self-confidence, you are able to resist the signals of distress that call for hurrying. The feeling is, **"...I can do everything God asks me to with the help of Christ who gives me the strength and power"** (Philippians 4:13, TLB). This kind of boldness and belief engenders and enlarges your faith.

Whenever unnecessary rushing takes place, it is indicative of the fact that your confidence, dedication and commitment are limited to the immediate, the temporal and the present. The older person must be able to go beyond the immediate, to traverse the temporal and to prevent the present from causing hurry-scurry. These areas are transcended through enlarged faith.

Through faith, your concept of life, worth and possibility is heightened and crystallized, thus broadening your potential power and capability. It is in and through your faith that belief, not only in your own ability and expertise, but also trust in and dependence upon a Higher Power [God], is generated.

"What is faith? It is the confident assurance that something we want is going to happen. It is the certainty that what we hope for is waiting for us, even though we cannot see it up ahead."

Hebrews 11:1 (TLB)

Pacing Yourself — A Faith Venture

Mastery of the ability to take your time is more than an act borne of decision. It is a reliance borne on the wings of commitment. Through trust and expectation, it is a venture into the realm of faith. Faith produces a divine assurance, unaccounted for in the natural, that surpasses all knowledge and awareness.

To take your time requires a deep sense of faith in the future. It cannot be adequately explained, and no one is sure how it works, but you are made to know that "all will be well."

This act of taking your time is also ideally, inexplicably and inextricably bound to and involved in trust in "Another." This "Other Person" is known and addressed by many names.

With this sense of presence, caring and protection, the person holding this faith in the Other One (the Father God) moves quietly, steadily, resolutely and unhurriedly forward. There is a sense of well being that Someone sees in the darkness of night and holds the morrow in strong and capable hands.

This kind of faith is highly essential toward the well being of the older person. As the years pass, loved ones scatter, children leave, friends diminish and all-around change takes place. Then comes a natural feeling of uncertainty, doubt and wonderment. This feeling can cause serious imaginations, bringing sleepless nights, restless hours and mental and emotional stress and unrest.

Practice Taking Your Time

Like most feats, taking your time comes with practice. The hurry-scurry times in which we live promote the feeling that if we don't hurry, we won't be able to keep up. The world will run away, and we will be left alone in its wake. This tendency misrepresents the facts. The faster the world turns, the greater the number of people who are left in its wake.

This multitude is not left behind in the sense that it is not of importance, productivity, or usefulness. Unbelievably, this group comprises the greater percentage of our society. The problem is two-fold: 1) Many do realize that they have been left behind by the fast pace; and 2) Others spend years, and in some cases, lifetimes trying to catch up with the front runners. Some fail while others partially succeed.

In the process of participation and matriculation in society, these people make contributions to the quality of life. This group, however, could be even more effective if it settled for a route just short of the fast track. They would probably live longer and enjoy the journey more, too. A philosopher once said, "The hurrier I go, the behinder I get."

When I was a child, my mother used to encourage me to learn or develop certain abilities by repeatedly saying, "Practice makes perfect." This may not be exactly true in the strictest sense, but it clearly sets for the basic principle in learning.

It is necessary that we do over and over that which we would learn to do better. Taking your time is not an easy thing to do, especially after years of rushing.

In order to master the technique of slowing your pace, older persons must practice.

A baseball pitcher throws thousands of pitches, the infielder chases many ground balls, and the outfielder runs after numerous fly balls. This is true with other sports. Professional shots at the basketball goal, passes, dribbles, catches, runs, tackles, putts and punches are all improved and made perfect through repetition. This is true in your quest for mastery over the body as well.

In Dale Apollo Cook's Karate School, there are forms, one corresponding to each belt graduation or promotion. These forms consist of a multiplicity of punches, turns, kicks, strikes, grabs, pulls, steps, jumps, sprints, splits and spirit yells. Personally, I have experienced much frustration, despair and mental anguish trying to cope with these forms. Through the wise counsel of my instructors and through observation, I have learned that nothing takes the place of repetitive practice. Learning to take your time also comes with repetitive practice.

It took time to learn to rush, and it takes time and practice to discipline yourself into better habits.

Let the World Come to You

"Stop the World, I Want to Get Off." This pop song denotes the concept of life and approach to it and its many issues by a great number of people. They choose not to be a part of the irrational, relentless race, yet they allow themselves to get caught up in it and later want to get out. They find themselves trapped in the whirl of things, and many develop the "If I don't run, I will get run over" syndrome. This, coupled with the fear of getting left behind, causes many people to press the panic button and ignite the spark of consternation and the winless race is on. They cannot keep up, fear being left behind and dare not discontinue.

Older people must resist these debilitating contingencies and determine to live a normal, relaxed, slow-paced life. Firm, resolute decision is a third of the victory; determination comprises a third; and tenacity and perseverance round out the final third.

People who rush about overextend themselves in their efforts to keep up or to stay atop the whirling world. They might be surprised at how much of that world might slow down to accommodate them if they ceased to be a participant in the race.

Like many of the things we feel must be done or all will fall apart, we worry and fret, lose sleep and grow gray hairs, only to find that the issue worked itself out satisfactorily without our help! This is also true of many of the issues and problems we face. They will work themselves out to our benefit, or they will become unessential.

A good admonition is the one which bids us to not take too seriously any issue, because a good percentage of the things we worry about will never happen. Another good percentage will work themselves out if left alone, which leaves only a small percentage of matters worth serious consideration.

Much time, thought and energy are expended in fear and worry over issues which cannot and need not be changed and which time, circumstances, or providence work out. The waste is further extended when the wear and tear on the mind and body through stress, strain and frustration are considered.

This principle became clear to me when our church, The Greater Mount Rose Baptist Church of Tulsa, Oklahoma, was displaced by the Tulsa Urban Renewal Authority. In order to meet the vacating deadline, it was necessary to have several novices help pack for moving. The many files, stacks and folders I had alphabetically and numerically arranged were indiscriminately boxed. After two years of wandering before the new facility was usable, I again came face to face with that mountain of materials to read, review and recheck piece by piece.

The interesting discovery was that of the numerous concerns, questions and problems that these communications covered, few needed addressing. Most of the challenges had worked out satisfactorily without my help. Others, over which I had great concern, never became a problem. Many situations work themselves out over a process of time.

The Merry-Go-Round Syndrome

Frequently, the merry-go-round is referred to as the entity which goes nowhere. The movement goes nowhere. There is, however, another side to the work of the merry-go-round. It could be said that it does the same thing so many times that it becomes perfect in its act.

Older persons can learn the secret of patience from the merry-go-round. They should be content to remain in the same place for as long as necessary. They should resist the temptation of boredom in retracing steps and going in the same circles, by finding fulfillment in serving and helping others in the normal day-to-day tasks.

Once the "take-your-time" task has been accomplished, each repetition, though subconsciously done, will bring the effort closer to the state of perfection. Then the older person is on the road to health and happiness, for the habit of rush, run and hurry is one of the giants to be destroyed before entry into the Canaan of health and body harmony.

You can live to be a hundred
If you can be happy,
With plenty of rest
And without stress.

Reasons Not to Rush

Some of the more common reasons why older people don't need to rush are:

1. There will be other meetings.

2. Often, the risk of life, property and reputation aren't necessary, because the meeting has not begun.

3. The business meeting can go on without you.

4. Better to miss the meeting than to make the morgue!

5. Rushing is the ace enemy of good health.

6. The meeting, matter, or money aren't the end of the world.

7. Better to be late for one meeting than not make the next one.

8. More often than not, in the final analysis, it was not necessary or profitable to rush.

9.   If you express regret for having to miss the meeting, people understand.

10.   If you miss the meeting, people say, "We missed you." If you are a fatality in a speeding accident or mishap, they say, "We miss him/her."

11.   We are not called to make new worlds, only to try to better this one.

12.   You don't have to keep up to run well; the meeting can go on without you. It will one day anyway.

13.   Time does not wait, but opportunity sometimes does.

14.   God did not rush when He made the world — or us.

15.   Rushing deletes deliberateness.

16.   The true purpose of the good life is not to get many things done in a hurry, but to do a few things well.

17.   The added risk of accident, injury and/or death is not worth it.

18.   The wise person thinks of some other approach or solution.

* * *

Poem
"Time Flies"
By Rev. Andrew D. Phillips

Everything comes slowly anymore,
    Except of birthdays, of course.
They seem to come in droves,
    No matter what their source.

I hardly get to sleep before it is day again.
   Then suddenly night is near.
I'm getting older every day,
   The longer I stay around here!

I go faster to catch up,
   And get the more behind.
Everyone's going around
   But I'll just stay in line.

Go around they may
   Going with all their might.
I'll come right along,
   Keeping them in sight.

The race is not given to the fastest,
   But to those who endure to the end.
Those who run and help someone,
   To higher heights ascend.

So time goes slow and time goes fast,
   It all adds up the same.
We live and learn and pass away,
   When we're finished playing life's game.

4

Avoid Fellowship With the Despairing

Electricity and human nature differ distinctly in that with electricity, like charges repel and unlike charges attract. With human nature, it is the opposite.

In the human family, in large measure, we are "who we run with." We are products of our environment and by-products of the company we keep. Someone has said, "Show me who you associate with, and I will tell you who you are." This is particularly true in the world of older people.

Hope, cheer, smiles, purpose, self-confidence and laughter are blessings of the good life, and all who associate with people who possess them take on their characteristics. Fear, doubt, purposelessness, hopelessness and dread are fallouts from the enemy of good will, and all who are influenced by them or follow people with these characteristics forfeit entry into the realm of quietude.

Although there are many blessings for the elderly who reside in nursing homes, one disadvantage is being subjected to the presence of a despairing society. *Despairing* means "the utter lack of hope."

If a person is to improve his/her health status in body, mind and spirit, there is a need for a healthy climate in which to pursue this quest.

While this associational arrangement cannot be avoided, it is nevertheless wise and healthy to avoid frequent and close association with those who give into and in some cases enjoy inability, disability and the loss of credibility.

We are by-products of our surroundings, outgrowths of our environment. If we want to be happy, we must seek to be in the company of happy people. It is easier to laugh if you are in the presence of others who laugh. Confidence and hope soar highest in an atmosphere of joy and laughter.

I feel old only when I am around older people who choose to be old because of increasing age; those who have decided to be old because some debilitating condition plagues their body; or because "I allow myself to think old."

Sometimes living is thought to be an agenda — a list of things that should happen here and here and here. We think it is what we see happening in other people's lives, and we assume that we should be on some kind of success schedule as well.

Young people believe they should accomplish certain things at certain times. After all, someone younger than they are cut quite a swatch at an early age. What they frequently do not realize is that this "wonder person" often has to begin all over and never quite reaches the same pinnacle again.

Older people have been led to believe they must break down by certain ages. Someone said their mental capacities would not be as sharp, but no one told them their wisdom increases. It is best not to listen to dark predictions and negative suggestions, but to speak words daily that they are getting better.

The best tonic for an older person is a younger person. The younger mind challenges the older. The younger body dares and drives the older to unsuspected and unbelievable feats. The younger spirit dreams of that which spurs greater heights. Older people should be encouraged to spend time with children, because the children give buoyancy to the physical, mental and spiritual capacities through their innocence, creativity and faith.

Psychologically, the best place to recuperate is not at the hospital or nursing home, but in your own home. The presence of the sick does little to strengthen or encourage the sick. Sitting on a bench at the park with other sitters or joining others rocking in the chair of "senior citizen consolation" or dragging yourself along because of a few discomforts will do little toward improving your status of health — mind, body, or spirit. On the other hand, mixing, mingling and competing with the alert, the strong and the young offer great dividends in all areas of desire and endeavor.

I believe that children were given for many reasons, but one is to help the old to remain or become young again. I love children. When I sit with older people, I feel older. When I play with children or younger people, I feel younger.

At the beginning of our Bible study session on Wednesday nights at The Greater Mount Rose Baptist Church in Tulsa, Oklahoma, we call the roll to ascertain the number present from each ministry group of the church. The recording secretary calls for the number of ministers, deacons, ushers, etc. I consistently vote with the ministers and the young adults. At first, the class took it as a joke or a gesture of wishful thinking. After several years, there is rarely even a smile of reaction. Identifying with the young makes me feel as one of them.

I believe grownups, and especially the older, stop playing kid games too early. Playing simple kid games, romping on the floor and seriously competing with children are rejuvenative tonics that rival medication.

Sometimes I felt silly and out of place stretched out on the floor playing jacks, tic-tac-toe, marbles and other kid games with my children. Sometimes it was uncomfortable and painful stooping, bending, reaching and stretching, but it has paid great recreative dividends. I can now stretch without feeling that I am breaking, and the resulting fun for the children and exercise for me are worth the effort.

Birds of a Feather Flock Together

The slogan has it that ''birds of a feather flock together.'' The person who wants to improve his/her health, spirit, faith and general outlook on life and concept of life must not flock, listen to, or interact with those who have lost hope in life.

There is no therapeutic essence in listening to someone ramble on and on about their sickness, pains, aches, broken parts and operations. Conversation on these maladies should be brief and replaced with the more cheerful, positive and promising aspects of life. This is for the good of both parties.

Whenever I visit the sick, my motive is to cheer them up, to spur them on to recovery and to assure them that they have good reason to feel positive about getting well. This cannot be accomplished if my mood is downcast, my disposition is one of sadness and the conversation is centered on what is wrong with them and how serious it is.

Some years ago, in a church in Daingerfield, Texas, to which I was called as pastor, a young woman approximately 22 years old was involved in an automobile accident that left her paralyzed from the waist down.

On my first visit to the church after accepting the call as pastor, I was told of this young woman's sad plight. How tragic, I thought. A young person just entering the prime of life was now sentenced, through a quirk of fate, to a possible lifetime in bed. I delayed my visit with her while I pondered what to say to her and how to say it. Should I ask her how it happened, was she in pain and if there was something I could do for her? Even more disturbing was the question, "What do I say to cheer her up and give her hope?"

I was still struggling with these questions when it came time to visit this young woman. With great reluctance, I entered the room and beheld a beautiful young woman with long silky hair; sparkling, confident eyes; and a radiant smile, molding her lovely face into a mass of seraphic humanity.

As I sought vainly for appropriate words, I was quickly rescued from my dilemma as she cheerfully greeted me. She reached for my hand, and as soon as she released it, she began the infant-like patting of her hands as she praised the Lord and told me over and over how good and merciful He was.

When I left her, I thanked God that, though she was sick, she made the well feel even more whole; she brought healing to broken dreams of many; and she caused others to appreciate their blessings which far exceeded hers.

As I mentioned earlier, in the field of electricity, like charges repel and unlike charges attract each other. Herein is a parallel to life. At best, life must be full of diversity, excitement, challenge and expectation. To achieve this, it is important that there be a mixture of these living values.

It is not what fate one encounters — whether illness, accident or old age — but it's how one adjusts, accepts and relates to the inevitability of some down sides to the roller coaster of life.

There is a war between age and death. Let us fight to be victors in the former before the latter wins out. This is especially needful for the older person and particularly for the sick and shut in. Sick people, like charges, repel, rebuff and retard each other.

Sick and well persons (unlike charges) tend to attract each other. Put another way, when healthy persons are in the continual presence of and in association with sick people, there is a natural tendency for the disposition of each to "rub off" on the other. The only exception is the nurses, doctors and others who work around the sick. The sick feel stronger and the well feel weaker. When the sick associate with the sick, despair results. When the weak is in the company of weakness, debilitation sets in. Whenever the aged spend too much time with the aged, particularly those who have given up hope, hopelessness sets in.

Because of this tendency, the sick need as much association with the healthy and the hearty as possible. Put the weak with the strong, the faithless with the faithful, the hopeless with the aspiring and the old with the young.

5
Keeping Well

Handshaking is perhaps the most common way that cold germs are passed from one person to another. The handshaking tradition is both a good and and bad practice. It is good in the sense that, short of the kiss, it is an intimate and socially-acceptable salutation. It is bad in the sense that it passes germs from one person to the next.

The hands pick up the germ; later, it is passed on to the body through rubbing the eyes, lips, or any tender part of the body and by eating food held by an unwashed, germ-infected hand. It is, then, of great importance that the hands are washed often to ward off this possibility.

If an ounce of prevention is worth a pound of cure, then a particle of carefulness is worth a world of correction.

Work At Keeping Well

It is easier to keep well than to get well. It pays great dividends to invest the time, money and energy required to improve and maintain a healthy status than to let the body wear down, lose its power of resistance and then try to build it up again.

The common cold, to older persons, is a great threat. The danger of "catching" a cold from breathing the room air of a person who has a cold or from riding in a car with such a person is minimal. However, the exposure to these living cells, coupled with other existing viruses in the body, can cause colds or other illnesses.

Most of the illnesses I have experienced through the years came from my own carelessness and failure to take the necessary precautions toward keeping well. Following a suggestion by my doctor, I keep a supply of mild mouth wash on hand, and without provocation or any particular need, I occasionally rinse my mouth to assist my body in fighting off cold and other germs. At the slightest sign of a cold or fever, I take one of the non-aspirin products. This procedure has remarkably improved my health and has been beneficial to my fight against the enemies to good health, such as colds, viruses, sleeplessness and exhaustion.

Sometimes the body is not ill, but is simply worn down and needs a rest. When the body grows older, it becomes more susceptible to illnesses precipitated by the elements of cold, wind, rain and other inclement influences. Hence, there is a need for special care and protection. During the winter months, many older people, in an effort to keep warm so they won't take cold, actually invite the problem by either dressing too heavily or overheating their home.

While being careful not to overheat your body or dwelling, care must be taken to protect the body from excessive and prolonged chill, dampness and other harmful exposure.

The three primary functions of the body — physical, mental and moral — work conjunctively and interactively in their natural quest of supporting, protecting and guarding each other. Whenever one element falters or gets into trouble, the other two are usually diminished or adversely affected. They lend themselves to the weak area. *Many people fall short of their mental and physical potential, because they fail to develop their moral and spiritual strengths.*

Illnesses and diseases usually take a greater toll on older persons and are usually harder to shake than for a younger person. For this reason, maintaining health is crucial to the older person.

Here are some practical suggestions for avoiding illness, particularly for the older person.

1. Avoid getting wet in the rain. Should this happen, change into warm clothing as soon as possible. After changing, remain in a warm place for at least one hour.

2. Get plenty of sleep. The amount of sleep required varies from person to person. One good yardstick of the need is whether you function better with five hours of sleep or eight hours. Once this is determined, consistently try to get that amount of sleep.

3. Take a short nap each day, midway between the time you awake and the time you retire. This nap serves as a regulator to guard against strain of the body. If the pull on the body has been more than normal, the nap will make up for it. If the body is weak, the nap adds to the strength and resistance needed to maintain a healthful status.

The nap need not be a lengthy one. Personally, I believe a short nap is more beneficial than a long one. A long nap tends to interfere with the regular night's sleep. A short nap gives recreated vigor to all capacities of the body, sharpening the intellect, reviving the physical and extending the vision of the spiritual.

4. Control eating habits. Eat light rather than heavy. The stomach does not have to be full to be happy. In fact, it is happier unfilled. It doesn't take much food to supply the necessary energy for a body that is not burning many calories.

When I was between 50 and 60 years of age, I was constantly plagued with colds and flu viruses, even during the spring and summer. During winter, it was difficult to carry out my duties as pastor of the church because of my frequent colds, which averaged about one cold per three-week period. Added to this were sore and dry throat and severe hoarseness that hampered my preaching and speaking.

I recall the time I had several maladies plaguing me at once: a skin rash, an ear infection, soreness in the rib cage below my heart, sleeplessness, stiffness, arthritis in my shoulders, an irritation in my nostril linings, besides the chronic colds.

I took "everything in the drug store" but to no avail! My precaution to prevent colds became an obsession. I tried to be careful, dodge the cold weather and avoid crowded rooms where I might contract a cold. In spite of all my efforts, the colds persisted.

With my new program of physical fitness through exercise, coupled with a new birth of spiritual endeavor, motivation and an improved concept of the good life, all of this has changed.

I now play games of softball, basketball and touch football with my children. I feel better than when I was 30 years of age!

I seldom have a cold because of the combination of my physical, mind and spiritual strengths, coupled with the other measures mentioned in this book. I am well and strong. My energy reserve, health and vitality are attributable to my "busy bee" lifestyle, spirit of genuine respect and love for fellow humans and an exhausting and self-challenging exercise program.

The human body was made for work. The first responsibility given to mankind was to work at dressing and keeping the Garden of Eden in which Adam lived. I think his work was not of the drudgery variety, but more of a recreational, pleasurable, fulfilling sort. Before sin entered, it was enjoyable dressing and keeping the garden. After sin came in, however, it became a chore, an unpleasant task, a burden and a drag. The first type of work referred to generated refreshment, recreation and pleasure; the second, disdain, displeasure and disquietude.

Our work today may be in the form of production, as work in a factory, office, store, or classroom; or it may be in the form of recreation or physical fitness. Whatever it is, it can have a positive impact and effect on one's body if accompanied by a healthy mindset and spirit.

If your work does not provide sufficient physical activity, then there is a need for more recreational or physical exercise. For happiness, contentment and fulfillment to prevail in your work, it should be complemented with a program of body fitness and exercise.

No Smoking, Drugs, or Alcohol

The older person who is wise will abstain from smoking, drugs and alcohol.

Smoking

Some people take the unwise and erroneous position that since there are persons who smoke regularly for years and are obviously not affected by it, smoking must be less than a high risk.

Body composition and tolerance are as diverse as skin pigmentation. What is good for the gander sometimes kills the goose. What is sauce for the sailor is strychnine for the soldier.

The smoker who lived a long life might have lived an even longer, healthier life had he not smoked.

There are some matters of health that a person should not have to be told by a doctor to abstain from. Smoking is one of them. A little common sense suggests that heated smoke, laced with unhealthy nicotine pulled rapidly into and coursing through the tender lining of the lungs, is unhealthy and even deadly.

Alcohol

Like smoking, alcohol might actually benefit the health of one person and kill another. Biological "make-up" has one person drinking excessively for years without any apparent adverse effect, while another person who drinks heavily or even moderately develops serious complications early on.

Observation, medical reports and common sense place us on the side of the abstainer. Except for the "medical" degree of alcohol included in "prescribed" medication, it is obvious and generally considered that the body is better off without the ingestion of alcohol, especially in large amounts and for older people.

Drugs

Except for those which are part of "prescribed" medication, drugs are off limits for the older person. The wise older person follows closely the "doctor's" orders and the "doctor's" counsel. A part of this counsel is that great care is to be taken in taking medication beyond that which is prescribed. Anything above "across-the-counter" medication — and not all or just any of that — is anathema for older people.

Drugs, like alcohol, are good or bad, depending upon their use. In one instance or use, a drug may lead to health or save one's life. In another, the same drug can destroy or kill.

Playing With Children

People grow old, not only because of the aging process, but because they sometimes forget the things that keep children young, such as freeheartedness, tenderness, lightheartedness, forgiveness, faith in the future, laughter, imagination and innocency.

Keeping Busy

Nothing grows old as fast as something in disuse. Automobiles run better and last longer if they are driven regularly. Houses depreciate faster when unoccupied. This is also true of the body, mind and spirit. For maximum productivity, they must be kept busy.

It is dangerous and ill-advised for an older person to become sedentary, because a degeneration process then sets in.

Keeping active through a program of exercise can be stressful and even painful, but the pain of exercise and other physical endeavor is far less than the pain of frozen and rheumatic joints, accompanied by other aches and pains caused by poor blood circulation and/or high blood pressure. The advantages of physical activity also include many other rewards.

Keep busy! Stretch your mental processes and the imagination. Belong to clubs, fraternities, athletic groups, churches, volunteer groups, etc. Be active and serve others. Nothing wards off the aging process and the "I'm too old" syndrome like keeping busy. It is surely better to die active than to die a gradual, painful death because of inferior body function.

Some of the more practical truths about keeping busy for the person who is growing older are:

* Go to worship services often. There is more than strength in the practice.

* Do a lot of activities with the family, friends, or even alone.

* Iron rusts when it is allowed to lay around.

* Sleep comes easier to a tired body.

* Appetite is better for a body which has burned calories.

* Read every chance you get.

* Help others in need.

Better than years tied to a rocking chair, walker, crutches, a nursing home, or hospital is to live and

conduct yourself so that, having worn yourself out
through service and good will toward God, you simply
hang out the sign, "Caught up with assignment and
moved on."

I'd rather .... *Than*

Leave	Linger
Wear out	Rust out
Be extinguished	Flicker
Cease	Sit
Die	Half Live

While I am keenly aware of the ever-present
temptation and tendency to overdo, I make it a point
to keep busy. My major and full-time profession and
work is pastor of The Greater Mount Rose Baptist
Church in the city of Tulsa. In addition to this service,
I serve as moderator for the Northwest Creek District
Association, President of the Martin Luther King
Commemoration Society, Homiletics instructor for the
Christian Ministers Alliance and instructor in the
Oklahoma School of Religion. I go to karate class twice
weekly and jog two miles three times a week in all
weather conditions. I also provide time for my wife and
two young children.

I choose to risk overdoing it rather than let my
body freeze up and lose its mobility and my mind
stagnate. The risk of overdoing, measured against the
benefit of a healthy existence, is minor in comparison.

In comparison to the physical body, the normal,
constant use of an automobile isn't what wears it out.
Instead, the most damaging wear and tear come from

the fast starts, the sudden stops, speeding and failure to properly maintain the car. When I try to put two days' work into one, I can feel the wear and tear on my body.

However, I have found that to keep busy is to keep healthy. Each person must determine his/her own physical ability and keep only as busy as that ability permits. But *keep busy* — too busy to become *stale, static, mean, bored,* or *old.* Stretch your *body, mind* and *spirit.* Be a *mover.* There is no need to die until the time comes to die. Live so you can count your living to have been a *lift* for life and death a *reward* for having given freely of *faithfulness.*

Life in the work place can be an unjust and frustrating rat race. How do we avoid the competitive rush without being irresponsible? What is a sensible approach to *earning a living?* The writer of Ecclesiastes offers an answer. He pictured as mistaken those who took the "me first" approach and plunged themselves into all kinds of activities that were aimed at getting more and doing better than anyone else, but he also declared it wrong when a person decided to *give up and drop out.*

> **"Again, I considered all travail, and every right work, that for this a man is envied of his neighbour. This is also vanity and vexation of spirit.**
>
> **"The fool foldeth his hands together, and eateth his own flesh."**
> **Ecclesiastes 4:4,5**

A sensible response lies between these two extremes. In contrast to the greedy and competitive person, we should reach out for one handful, not two.

> **"Better is an handful with quietness, than both the hands full with travail and vexation of spirit."**
> **Ecclesiastes 4:6**

Both those who drop out and those who attempt to outdo everyone else show a lack of trust in God.

Why should we rely on God? Because only when we come to know Him through Jesus Christ can we develop confidence in His power, wisdom and goodness, no matter how senseless life may seem. This gives us peace and hope.

Dying is something we either just do or something we have to do. It all depends on how we live!

Keeping Well Test

1. Are you sometimes careless about putting your hands to parts of your face after shaking hands with someone and you haven't washed your hands?

2. Are you sometimes careless about the care of your body through unnecessary exposure? (Example: Not wearing sufficient clothing, not taking proper care and precaution after getting wet, etc.?)

3. Do you sometimes refuse to reduce the pace and get more rest when cold symptoms come to you?

4. Have you not determined how much sleep your body thrives best on?

5. Do you not take time for a daytime nap?

6. Do you sometimes overeat?

7. Do you often eat that which is not good for your health?

8. Are you inactive most of the time?

9. Do you never or very seldom play with children?

10. Do you not engage in a program of regular exercise?

11.   Do you find yourself worrying a lot?

12.   Are you easily upset or irritated?

13.   Do you worry or fear that you might be sick or die?

14.   Do you spend a lot of time regretting things of the past?

15.   Do you spend a lot of time wishing empty wishes? Example A: You wish you could be young again, or you could relive some mistakes. Example B: You blame yourself for things that went wrong.

16.   Do you spend a lot of time wondering if you have done and are now doing things right?

(Grade yourself and work on improving.)

6

Let Laughter Dominate Your Heart

Because society has been computerized to expect older persons to be stoic, passive, sour and generally of an irritable nature, many older people subconsciously tend to voluntarily accommodate this image. This is unfortunate, for in the heart of every person, regardless of age, is the potential of joy, light-heartedness and laughter.

What to say, common sense as to how to say it and knowledge of when to say it in a combination will make an older person the life of the party and a joy to be around!

The negative, evil and destructive agents of life which cause, promote and maintain sickness, pain, sorrow and all the other downs and darknesses of existence, were acquired through the fall of Adam. The positive, joyous, inspiring and invigorating agents which give rise to hope, health, happiness, healing and all the other pluses and ups were given by God in the formation of man. Among these were smiles and laughter. There can be little doubt of the truth of this fact. You have only to observe it.

Notice the difference in the physical effects of a smile and a frown:

* The smile invigorates; the frown debilitates.

* The smile makes the frown break.

* The smile strengthens; the frown weakens.

* The smile inspires; the frown induces fainting.

* The smile encourages; the frown discourages.

* The smile produces growth; the frown stunts growth.

* The smile engenders faith; the frown produces doubt.

* The smile broadens the horizon of life; the frown limits the view of the soul.

* The smile honors God; the frown pleases satan.

* The smile illuminates; the frown darkens.

* The smile assures; the frown confuses.

* The smile blesses; the frown curses.

* The smile promotes; the frown retards.

* The smile generates positivism; the frown gives birth to negativism.

* The smile frees; the frown enslaves.

Smiles and laughter are contagious and permeate life with a positiveness that enriches and enlivens. Wherever there is laughter, there is inspiration, confidence and hope. Laugh *with yourself, by yourself* and *at yourself. Laugh* and *God laughs with you. Frown* and the *devil frowns upon you.*

Laughter is:

1.   What the soul longs for, but it cannot generate on its own.

2.   What God provided for difficult times.

3.   Music to the senses.

4.   That which moves mountains when sheer strength cannot.

5.   A free gift that gives equally to everyone.

6.   Food for the soul, a restorer of energy and a regulator for the heart.

7.   Good news in the night of trouble.

8.   What the poor uses when the rich takes everything else.

9.   The release valve of pent-up emotions.

10.   Hope expressed in non-verbal language.

11.   The difference between weakness and strength, success and failure.

12.   What carries on when all else is gone.

13.   Daylight during night seasons.

14.   Spiritual medication.

15.   Common sense graduation.

16.   That which makes one rich without money.

17.   What makes the poor equal to the rich and the weak equal to the strong.

18.   What gives two days' life for one night's darkness.

19.   Hope for the journey and light for the path.

20.   What provides a common denominator between the young and the old.

Benefits of Laughter:

It:

1. Helps the sick get well.

2. Gives strength to the weak.

3. Gives hope to the despairing.

4. Fills the emptiness of meaninglessness with meaning and purpose.

5. Replenishes the weariness of soul and gives fleeting to the feet of facility.

6. Helps make Christianity real.

7. Crosses racial, cultural, religious and ethnic boundaries.

8. Gives animating assurance to debilitating doubt.

9. Helps make life worth living.

10. Invigorates when ineffectiveness has taken over.

11. Slows down the aging process.

12. Makes life easier.

13. Is as sun rays in the midst of storms.

14. Is the dessert of the meal of life.

15. Shortens the long journey.

16. Provides dividends of health incentive.

17. Does battle with the aging process.

18. Is a dynamo of encouragement.

19. Rains assurance during the drought of discouragement.

20. Is what frowns wish for.

21. Is a faith finder.

22. Generates what frowns fight for.

23. Is a message from angels.

24. Bridges the chasm of time, and joins the temporal to the eternal.

25. Speaks where words are forbidden.

26. Dwells where words find emptiness.

Longfellow said, "Into each life some rain must fall." The rain may be in the form of the loss of assets, the loss of a loved one, a crippling accident, a broken home or marriage, sickness or just the pains, discomforts and disadvantages of old age.

There is only one way to avoid the difficulties of old age and that is to die early. There is, however, a measurable alternative, which is to learn how to grow older in an enjoyable manner. This process of learning might well begin with adjusting to the rains of life.

The rain causes some people to become bitter, coarse and irritable, while others mellow and become warm and compassionate toward others. The rain causes some people to become old before their time, to hurt more than they need to and to make life miserable for themselves and others around them.

Others more wisely set about to defy the aging process by playing young games, playing with young children, being productive and useful, thinking young and encompassing their lives with the inculcation of a full function of the three powers of existence — *physical, mental* and *spiritual.*

Keep Smiling!

If smiling can prevent wrinkles, surely it can slow down the aging process. *The face televises what is playing on the television of the soul.* Too many people allow their minds to become old, narrow, sightless, cold and polluted with negativism. The soul is housed by the body, and the face is the picture window of this house. Whatever the condition of the soul, the *face window* radiates it. It is, therefore, critical that the soul be fed the kind of food that will affect healthy maintenance and growth.

Although a hypocritical stance would not be advised, someone once said it is inspiring and stimulating for the person to train the face to smile!

Life has a boomerang effect built into it by the Creator. In a very real and true sense, *what one gives out* comes back to the *giver*, although it may take a period of time and present itself in various forms. So, if you practice smiling, it does two important and rewarding things:

1.   It feeds the soul with the vitamin of *positivism*, which tends to grow into a good way.

2.   It sends wave lengths of *pleasantness, joy, inspiration, hope, assurance* and *faith* that come back in many forms to reward the giver as much or even more than the receiver.

In his wisdom, the great preacher of Ecclesiastes advised this concept long ago:

> **"Cast thy bread upon the waters: for thou shalt find it after many days"**
> **Ecclesiastes 11:1**

The Master of the universe, the Lord of the world and the Word itself support this concept. Jesus' admonition in Luke 6:38 says:

"Give, and it shall be given unto you; good measure, pressed down, and shaken together, and running over, shall men give into your bosom. For with the same measure that ye mete withal it shall be measured to you again."

John Masefield expressed it well in "Laugh and Be Merry":

"Laugh and be merry. Remember, better the world with a song.

"Better the world with a blow in the teeth of a wrong.

"Laugh, for the time is brief, a thread the length of a span.

"Laugh and be proud to belong to the old proud pageant of man.

"Laugh and be merry, remembering in older time,

"God made heaven and earth, for joy He took in a rhyme,

"Made them, and filled them full with the strong red wine of His mirth.

"The splendid joy of the stars; the joy of the earth.

"So we must laugh and drink from the deep blue cup of the sky,

"Join the jubilant song of the great stars weeping by,

"Laugh, and battle, and work, and drink of the wine outpoured,

"In the dear green earth, the sign of the joy of the Lord.

"Laugh and be merry together, like brothers akin,

"Guests in a while in the rooms of a beautiful inn.

"Glad till the dancing stops, and the lilt of the music ends.

"Laugh until the game is played; and be you merry, my friends."[1]

[1] Earnest, Edward, Ed. *The Family Album of Favorite Poems,* (New York: Grosset and Dunlap, 1959), p. 21.

7

Proper Rest and Relaxation

I have had to learn two basic principles about growing older:

1.   While the old horse may not be what he used to be, he must nonetheless keep active, alert and busy! The horse, the person, the machine that stops progressing becomes victim to idleness, stagnation and inactivity.

It is incumbent upon older people to stretch and force their bodies into regular, guided, consistent and controlled exercise. This must be done even to a degree of discomfort, stress and pain. With this practice, the body toughens, adjusts, accepts and benefits. Without it, the body wilts, rejects, resists, loses and becomes old before its time.

2.   The older the horse, the more rest he must have. As a person grows older, usually from disuse, his/her metabolism slows and the respiratory system weakens. This usually happens from an unnecessary and unwarranted reduction of exercise and recreation. However, regardless of the reason, the aftereffects are the same. When this happens, the body calls for more rest and relaxation, the process of replenishment or catch up.

Consequences of Improper
Rest and Relaxation

If proper rest and relaxation are not given to the older person, serious consequences may result. Among them are:

1.   *Susceptibility to viruses:* Until recent years, I was frequently hindered by aggravating and agonizing colds. After much suffering, I realized that my body, like an older car or horse, required more rest and maintenance. The maintenance comes in the form of quality food, wholesome and inspiring surroundings and regular exercise. The rest comes in a package of its own.

2.   *Overexertion — a lack of the restorative process increases the aging process.* The body of an older person thrives, survives and materializes into its best self with proper exercise, rest and relaxation. Without proper exercise, rest and relaxation, the body is affected negatively.

It is a well-known fact that all that seems to be or promises to be restful is not. Watching television may not be as restful as it might appear to be. A visit or vacation may be many things other than rest. Every person is a trichotomy of human and divine family unity: body, mind and spirit. These family members interact, respect and support each other, regardless of what humanity tries through its carnal will to impose or create. For rest to take place, the entire person must be involved: body, mind and spirit.

Fishing may be a restful sport, recreation, or pastime, but if the body is sitting on the bank or in the boat and the mind is engrossed in unpaid bills or a personal or family problem, it is impossible for either the mind or the body to rest.

Joyce Hifler says it better in, *Think on These Things:*

"If you are out to waste your time, don't go fishing. It requires a calm patience that slows the motor, calms the blood pressure and holds the mind serene. Anything we love doing loves us. It settles us down to a normal rate so that our bodies and spirits can recenter themselves. It rests and reawakens us to new possibilities because, in our state of restfulness, we can think more clearly.

"Fishing is never just a pastime, but an investment. It reels in more than a catch, and when we pack up our gear to go home, we leave something behind — a worried mind. A few hours away from the hassle makes fishing a must, and it should have a regular place in our schedule."[1]

This is why the place of religion, treated in the next chapter, is of great importance to the individual, especially to the older person. Religious conviction, spiritual strength and providential proclivity are bedrock essential in bringing about the degree of tranquility, assurance and contentment needed for mind and body relaxation and rest.

Whether fishing, hunting, swimming, strolling, or vacationing, in order to bring about a true rest, the ability to achieve combined repose must be accomplished.

Two Avenues to Contentment and Happiness

There are two primary avenues to contentment and happiness:

---

[1] *The Tulsa World,* December 19, 1990, p. A-22.

First, *commitment to a higher providential order.* The supreme need for a deep religious conviction, belief and faith is paramount in the life of every individual, and especially in older persons.

An older person particularly, because of social changes, feels the hours of heaviness, lengths of loneliness, areas of aloneness, periods of pain and seasons of solitude. It is imperative that a person know God and His Son, Jesus Christ, in a personal relationship as a source of sustainment.

Call it whatever you will, but it must be a Source higher than all others in a person's experience and conception, one with a historical reputation of power and performance. Then, there must be complete commitment and allegiance to this Source — the Father of the Universe. This heavenly high tower or hideaway becomes the person's refuge.

When friends fail, assurance fades and hope dims, transference is then made to this "secret place" of the Most High, God Himself. There is no substitute for this Reference, Refresher, Rewarder, or Redeemer.

Psalm 91:1,2 says it best:

"He that dwelleth in the secret place of the most High shall abide under the shadow of the Almighty.

"I will say of the Lord, He is my refuge and my fortress: my God; in him will I trust."

The second avenue to happiness and contentment is *the determination to have it!* **"For as he thinketh in his heart, so is he..."** (Proverbs 23:7). Translated, this could read, *"As an older person thinks in his heart, so is he."* If he thinks he can, he can; if he thinks well, he tends to be well; if he thinks old, he is old; if he thinks young, it makes the person young in heart, in spirit, in health.

If you see life in a beautiful light, then life will be beautiful, because your belief will help to make it so.

William James said, ''This life is worth living, we can say, since it is what we make it, from the moral point of view.

''If this life be not a fight, in which something is eternally gained for the universe by success, it is no better than a game of private theatricals from which one may withdraw at will. But it feels like a real fight.

''Be not afraid of life. Believe that life is worth living, and your belief will help create the fact.''[2]

Tryon Edwards said, ''Happiness is like manna; it is to be gathered in grains, and enjoyed every day. It will not keep; it cannot be accumulated; nor have we got to go out of ourselves or into remote places to gather it, since it is rained down from Heaven, at our very doors.''[3]

Benjamin Franklin said, ''Alternatives — There are two ways of being happy, we may either diminish our wants or augment our means. Either will do, the result is the same. And it is for each man to decide for himself, and do that which happens to be the easiest. If you are idle or sick or poor, however hard it may be for you to diminish your wants, it will be harder

---

[2] Bartlett, John. *Familiar Quotations,* Toronto, Canada: Little, Brown & Company, 1937, 1948, 1955, 1965, 1968, 1980, p. 649.

[3] *Leaves of Gold,* Revised Edition. Williamsport, Pennsylvania: The Coslett Publishing Co., 1938, Revised 1948, p. 22.

to augment your means. If you are active and prosperous or young or in good health, it may be easier for you to augment your means than to diminish your wants. But if you are wise, you will do both at the same time, young or old, rich or poor, sick or well. And if you are very wise, you will do both in such a way as to augment the general happiness of society."[4]

---

[4] *Ibid.*, p. 81.

8

Resources and Rewards of Religion

Because of what religion is, every person and particularly older people, should have a concept of it. In plain and simple language, religion is belief in and paying allegiance to God Almighty, a super human, or super power, credited with creative, governing and sustaining powers.

Augustine wrote, ''Where the Search Ends — I searched the world over for God and found Him in my heart. In the heart of the believer a still small voice speaks in clearest accents, bearing 'witness with our spirits that we are the children of God.' Nothing on earth is so heavenly as that — so like 'the voice of angels singing in the silence.' It is as clear as bells at eventime. It is assuring like the familiar voice of a friend beloved. The Holy Spirit speaking in the secret chambers of the heart is the climax of God's revelation to us!''[1]

If the Creator, Maker, Organizer, Super Human is benefitted by having the created as a love object, then

---

[1] *Leaves of Gold*, Revised Edition. Williamsport, Pennsylvania: The Coslett Publishing Company, 1938, Revised, 1948, p. 108.

the creature benefits even more. The Maker makes the "creature" for His glory and honor, and gives him unlimited gifts, needs, desires and capabilities through which he may achieve improved, Maker-like status.

In young life, the carefree spirit, the many interesting challenges and the various interests serve to keep life alive and motivated. When age moves a person out of the sphere of the facilitators, replacement is necessary so that life does not become empty, meaningless and burdensome. Religion helps serve this need.

Having Someone in whom to believe helps one believe in himself/herself. Feeling the power of a Super Power gives one unknown, unbelievable and unlimited personal power, and being a part of the Great Spirit, the Holy Spirit, provides untold and uncontested fellowship and companionship of a variety known only to those who dare to embrace and invest in the realm of religion.

The older person, then, is wise to establish a strong, Biblical, sound and personal approach to religion, for in doing so, life in its later years has greater promise of joy and happiness.

Say whatever you wish, it will not change the obvious fact that society is in a moral dilemma of which it is incapable of extricating itself. Worse than this is the fact that society has reached a point at which it no longer feels a need for change.

The truth is, society is in rebellion of a Moral Law, and for its own benefit needs to change. The victims of this tragic trap of rebellion spend much time naming and debating its instigator or originator. Some refer to it as moral degeneracy, others refer to it as sin, and still others as social disorder. Whatever name is applied, the effects, results and penalties are the same. Whatever it is called, the rebellion and opposition against the law and order of God must be accounted for.

With religion, there must be a Higher Power, which is higher than its subjects. This Power is *supreme, self-contained, pre-existent* to all things present, eternal, omniscient, omnipotent and omnipresent — else, how can He be of benefit to the subject?

William James (1842 - 1910) reminds us that the question of having moral beliefs or not having them is decided by our wills. The heart must want a world of morality or the head will never make us want one. Religion is a case of winning in the end or losing all. There is no bell that tolls to warn us when truth is within our grasp. We, then, must not wait for the bell.

Frederick W. Robertson said, "There are three great principles in life which weave its warp and woof, apparently incompatible with each other, yet they harmonize and in their blending create this strange life of ours. The first is, 'Our fate is in our own hands, and our blessedness and misery the exact result of our own acts.' The second is, 'There is a divinity that shapes our ends, rough-hew them how we will.' The third is, 'The race is not to the swift, nor the battle to the strong; but time and chance happeneth to them all.' Accident, human will, the shaping will of Deity — these things make up life."[2]

---

[2] *Leaves of Gold*, Revised Edition. Williamsport, Pennsylvania: The Coslett Publishing Company, 1938, Revised 1948, p. 188.

Biblical Reality of A Higher Power —
The God of the Universe

A Biblical case in point is to be found in 1 Kings 18. A contest is waged between Elijah and the prophets of Baal to see whose God would answer by fire. In the midst of this moving drama and the partitioning of the prophets of Baal, Elijah accuses their god of being in conversation with someone else, and therefore, could not listen to both of them at the same time, or of pursuing his regular range of frequency, or of being asleep.

> "And they took the bullock which was given them, and they dressed it, and called on the name of Baal from morning even until noon, saying, O Baal, hear us. But there was no voice, nor any that answered. And they leaped upon the altar which was made.
>
> "And it came to pass at noon, that Elijah mocked them, and said, Cry aloud: for he is a god; either he is talking, or he is pursuing, or he is in a journey, or peradventure he sleepeth, and must be awaked."
>
> **1 Kings 18:26,27**

The Psalmist David declares that these "idol" gods are helpless.

> "Their idols are silver and gold, the work of men's hands.
>
> "They have mouths, but they speak not: eyes have they, but they see not:
>
> "They have ears, but they hear not: noses have they, but they smell not:
>
> "They have hands, but they handle not: feet have they, but they walk not: neither speak they through their throat."
>
> **Psalm 115:4-7**

David speaks of the idols again in Psalm 135:15-17:

"The idols of the heathen are silver and gold, the work of men's hands.

"They have mouths, but they speak not; eyes have they, but they see not;

"They have ears, but they hear not; neither is there any breath in their mouths."

Belief in, association with and allegiance is a personal matter. Each person must choose a person or form of God or god. Personally, I choose the God of the Bible, represented as the Judeo-Christian Creator of the world.

It is my personal opinion that this God qualifies as truly *supreme, holy, everlasting, eternal, self-contained, omnipresent, omniscient, historical and able* to save and serve all the needs of His creatures and creations. The older person would do well to associate himself with this God.

Joshua said:

"Now therefore fear the Lord, and serve him in sincerity and in truth: and put away the gods which your fathers served on the other side of the flood, and in Egypt; and serve ye the Lord.

"And if it seem evil unto you to serve the Lord, choose you this day whom ye will serve; whether the gods which your fathers served that were on the other side of the flood, or the gods of the Amorites, in whose land ye dwell: but as for me and my house, we will serve the Lord."

Joshua 24:14,15

Criteria for Choosing a Religion

Much study, investigation, attention and care must be given to the choice of religion. You should embrace at least three things:

1. What does the religion offer or promise in this present life?

2. What does the religion offer or promise concerning the afterlife, if there is one?

3. Who or what God, god entity, or power supports and sustains the religion?

By our definition, everyone embraces a religion.

It is impossible for a person with a sound mind to occupy time, space and being in this universe and not entertain some concept, belief and faith in and commitment to some power other than and above self.

One invests a lot in a religion and, therefore, has a right to expect a lot in return.

Some good questions to ask of a religion are:

1. What benefits do I derive from my religion?

2. What does it do for me physically?

3. What does it do for me spiritually?

4. Does its teachings make sense?

5. Does it make positive and moral demands on me?

6. Does it seek to better my life?

7. Does it involve my neighbor in a moral way?

8. Does it seek to control my moral conduct?

9. Does it seek a peaceful society?

Benefits of a Spiritual Relationship With God

The older person should seek a religious affiliation which is friendly or compatible with the previous nine questions.

As age increases, other interests, involvements and rewarding engagements will lessen. At this point, the older person needs moral, psychological and sociological replacement.

Years ago, older black people frequently sang hymns. One of them carried these words, "Religion never was designed to make our pleasures less." In other words, they expected more than a mere notion out of the religion they embraced. A religion that cares about its subject not only offers "pie-in-the-sky" benefits, but it also provides membership rewards in the here and now.

What Does Religion Do For Me Physically?

As I have previously mentioned, man is a trichotomy of body, mind and spirit.

Mankind's first concern is for the physical being. As a baby, the first concern is for physical care, even to the point of extreme selfishness. As we grow older, we grow into a broader concern, which includes other people, but even at best, we never rise above the natural concern for the physical body.

This desire for protection carries over into the realm of religion.

People, particularly older people, want and seek for a religion that serves their physical needs as well as their spiritual needs. The Bible gives evidence that the Master, Jesus Christ, expressed and demonstrated concern for the whole person. The following references indicate this.

Mark 9:19 — "...bring him unto me."

John 12:7 — "...Let her alone...."

Matthew 14:16 — "...give ye them to eat."

Matthew 10:8 — "Heal the sick, cleanse the lepers, raise the dead, cast out devils: freely ye have received, freely give."

The religion of the older person must be a "here and now" religion — one which helps in the day-to-day struggles of life. It is not too much to ask of a religion that it help with the physical vicissitudes and adversities.

The demonic powers of old manifest in materialistic, social and moral temptation. These evil forces sometimes activate themselves upon the physical man, causing pain, discomfort, distress and disabilities. At this point, a power greater than that of the individual is needed. This power is to be found in the proper and true religion, backed, supported and sustained by a proper and true God.

With this relationship, the maladies of older age are lessened and their intensity diminished. Religion teaches patience, stimulates strength and toughens faith. It **"beareth all things, believeth all things, hopeth all things, endureth all things"** (1 Corinthians 13:7).

What Does Religion Do for Me Spiritually?

A religion which does not prepare you for the hereafter is not worth its salt. Matthew 5:13 says, **"...if the salt have lost his savour, wherewith shall it be salted? it is thenceforth good for nothing, but to be cast out, and to be trodden under foot of men."**

There must be a God and a hereafter; otherwise:

1.   The Creator of an orderly, systematic, coordinated, punctual universe could not keep it in order afterwards.

2.   He then Who created the intricate, unmatchable man, didn't have sense or care enough to plan for his good.

3.   Order divided by intelligence = chaos.

4.   Much = nothing, and nothing is all there is.

5.   Time programmed itself but couldn't enter eternity.

6.   It all started without beginning.

7.   There was a clock of time that wound itself.

8.   It requires high intelligence to maintain a world order, but it was not needed for creation.

9.   We die to more and worse than we came from.

10.   Life is a joke, having been dead all the time.

11.   Humanity owes nobody apology for its existence, because there is no one intelligent enough to rationalize it.

12.   Nothing times nothing multiplied by nobody = people and places and time.

13.   Man is a god, created himself, and is therefore the only god there is.

14.   There is nothing moral about man; therefore, he is of no good.

15.   Mass is more important than man. Hence, the emphasis on materialism.

Man is the making of a Master Maker and Mastermind, and God then is undeniable.

Created With What?

The built-in radar system of the eye causes the eye to involuntarily bat when an object passes close in front of it, but does not when an object passes at a distance.

The birth instinct of a monkey, which causes it to back away from a cliff, is placed in the monkey in its early infancy.

The ability of a baby is to learn to speak a difficult language just from hearing it and observing lip language.

The fact that man was made to speak, who decided that dogs would bark, birds would tweet, lions would roar, bears would growl and snakes would hiss?

Who or what accounts for the perfect seasons, time and rotation system of the universe?

If this honor is to be credited to something other than a Person, then let the world, the people and the spirits require this "thing" to say more and to reveal itself in some manifestation.

What accounts for the progression and perpetuation of life? Can anything other than Life give life?

The absence of a documented Bible denies the historicity of the Man, Christ Jesus.

There is a need for a plot to disclaim His resurrection.

Where did the concepts of the prehistoric, pre-Christian era, religions of mankind originate?

Think of the inability of the world's greatest powers throughout history to dampen this religious force and fervor, not to speak of silencing or destroying it.

Death is perhaps the strongest of all earthly forces, and even its ravaging devastations have not deterred those who *believed* and *knew*. Death was administered through leaping lions, fiery furnaces, sharp swords, ferocious beasts, the chopping ax, the boiling water, stonings, burnings at stakes and crucifixion. Not one, nor all of these, have deterred the minds of those committed to the way of the One who said, "...I am the way, the truth, and the life..." (John 14:6).

Consideration must be given to the many who have died with Jesus' name on their lips. Attention must be given to the only One who dared to predict, promise and claim to have arisen from the dead.

Older persons would do well to lay hold on a religion that:

1. Does something for them spiritually. There is little doubt that a part of every person is a spirit. That part needs, desires and requires association with the Holy Spirit.

2. Observes that a life without a sense of purpose and expectancy is worse than waste. A good religion gives you life and more.

3. With nothing to complement it, is not worth having.

4. Represents the *anticipated love* of the Creator.

5. Does not come apart when stressed.

6. Stands on its own feet of belief.

7. Does not need to crush another to sustain itself.

8. Has greater joy in existence than in authority.

9. Gives a certain degree of satisfaction regardless of circumstances or conditions.

10. Pulls spirit, soul and body together in one unit.

Positive Don'ts:

1. Don't worry; it doesn't help.

2. Don't hold a grudge or anger. Anger hurts only the holder of it.

3. Don't let things get under your skin. There isn't room there!

4. Don't be irritable or you will irritate others.

5. Don't seek revenge. The moral law takes care of all.

6. Don't exert too much too quickly, or your time may exceed your energy.

7. Don't neglect the spiritual values. They are the only lasting ones.

8. Don't overeat. There will be other meals.

9. Don't hesitate to forgive. You will need it sometime!

10. Don't worry even if it does seem to help. You can get the same results without worry.

11. Don't hurt other people. It doesn't help you.

12. Don't think you are the only right person. You might be the only one wrong!

13. Don't be afraid to look at what someone else sees. You might like the sight.

14. Don't be afraid to look at yourself. You might be surprised at what you see.

15. Don't pray only for the sins of others. This is self-discrimination.

16. Don't live to yourself. There will come a time when you will need others to live with you.

17.   Don't shut others out, for in doing so, you shut yourself in.

18.   Don't pass up the need of another. You might be the one in need next time.

19.   Don't ignore a need, for that need will become yours.

20.   Don't take life lightly, or it will respond in kind.

21.   Don't expect more than you give. This is against the moral law.

22.   Don't expect more than you give. The Source will not accommodate.

23.   Don't forget to help others, for therein lies your help.

24.   Don't forget to bless others or blessings may forget you.

25.   Don't wonder if right wins. Just know that wrong doesn't.

26.   Don't fight with an adversary. Win over him.

27.   Don't look down. There is more to see above.

28.   Don't piddle in the dirt when there are stars to be hung.

29.   Don't fuss about fiddles when the band is already playing.

30.   Don't let anyone spoil your day. Make it yourself.

31.   Don't try to graduate from life. It will put you back in first grade.

32.   Don't pamper yourself. You are not a baby.

33.   Don't overrate yourself. You will be alone in the process.

34.   Don't be too religious. That's not good religion.

35.   Don't think you are special with God unless He is special with you.

36.   Don't let your head get too big from anything but natural head growth!

37.   Don't brag. You had help.

38.   Don't procrastinate, the clock is running.

39.   Don't do wrong. Right will judge.

40.   Don't fuss about the view. Raise your sights.

41.   Don't destroy the building of society. You live in it.

42.   Don't encourage hate; it breeds itself.

43.   Don't teach your children to hate, there will be plenty.

44.   Don't hate. Hate begets hate.

45.   Don't ignore God. He might confirm it.

46.   Don't play with death, because it plays for keeps.

47.   Don't criticize the view. Clean it up.

48.   Don't oil the wheels of hate. It runs well on its own.

God has not given us a moral code through which to save us, but to shield us from the suffering that is brought upon us through the scheme of the universe.

* * *

Poem
"Religion"
By Rev. Andrew D. Phillips

Religion is no great big thing,
    Mostly do's and don'ts.
Don't say what you don't want said,
    And give out what one does not want.

Do a little good however you can.
    Spread some sunshine here and there.
Help someone find happiness, dispel the
    gloom,
    Turn grey skies blue, foul weather fair.

As you wish that others would,
    Do ye even so to them.
Give to them who are in need,
    And should one fall, then turn to him.

The soul does not thrive on "things,"
    But the unseen from above.
This is why spiritual wings,
    Must be fueled with love.

Singing, preaching, praying,
    All may be just things, my friend.
But it's how you treat your fellow man
    That really counts in the end!

9

Care of the Crippled

Arthritis and rheumatic diseases affect millions of people each year and cost millions of dollars, much of which is paid by persons who would benefit more in using these dollars for food, clothing, exercise and education.

There are over a hundred different arthritic conditions, and treatment for these conditions varies.

A treatment that helps one person or type of disease will not work with another type or person. For this reason, careful diagnosis for each case is of great importance.

Several weeks of treatment are sometimes necessary to find relief and a cure. However, with care, common sense and a doctor's help, effective solutions are attainable today.

Medication

There are numerous over-the-counter medications. Among them are those which bring relief to certain rheumatic diseases. While there is an inherent danger in taking over-the-counter medications, through careful, discretionary experiments, you may find a medication that will work for you.

Should the slightest side effect develop, however, use should be discontinued immediately. While over-the-counter medications are a practical approach to help, the better approach is to consult your physician and follow through on his/her diagnosis, instructions and treatment.

Relaxation

The art of relaxation is what I call a *reacquired mentality.*

When we were little children, we had no problem relaxing. It came as naturally as seeing, hearing, sleeping, or eating.

So relaxed were we that we never worried or concerned ourselves about any matter for very long. We could let go and leave be. We could pray about and pack away our troubles and problems. We could *forgive and forget.*

Although I dealt on relaxation in a previous chapter, I would like to touch on this area again because of its importance.

Jesus said, **"...Except ye be converted, and become as little children, ye shall not enter into the kingdom of heaven"** (Matthew 18:3).

The cares of this world, *things, fears, faithlessness,* precipitated estrangement or distance from God and left us with a malady of *adultism* or *adult crisis.*

We must return to the childhood fearless faith and caring trust that overcome all barriers to complete relaxation.

As in the case of learning to take your time, it is also necessary that you practice if true relaxation is to be acquired.

Soul Security

The mind is, to a great extent, controlled by the emotions, and the emotions run wild unless they are anchored solidly in a certain Security.

As stated earlier, that Certain Security and Solid Assurance come only through a strong belief, faith and an undaunted commitment and devotion to a Higher Power — the Master of the Universe.

This belief in, reliance and dependence upon this Able One assures you that "all is well," that *there will be a tomorrow* and that tomorrow, though it might have some rain clouds and even some storms, will also have sunshine. With this faith in the future, this assurance through a Savior, you are able to bring the mind and emotions under control. Then the body follows and relaxation is accomplished.

Like most worthwhile ventures, the art of relaxation must be practiced. Relaxation is not simply a thought through which you decide to relax and then it is done. Both the mind and body must be trained and taught, and this process is best attained through discipline and persistent practice.

Exercise

There is no substitute for exercise. The rewards that come from exercise cannot be achieved through any other means. Many people try to attain the maximum benefits of exercise through a skippy, heartless, lazy, minimum amount of exercise, but the rewards and benefits of exercise are in direct proportion to the amount of exercise done. Now, this does not mean that each person must take the same type or amount of exercise, but that each must give an honest, serious and full measure of devotion to an exercise program that pulls the body and mind to their immediate limits.

Arthritis is painful, and pain causes muscles to become tight and tense. If the muscles are left in this tired and immobile state, they tend to freeze, and the problem is progressively worsened. The only long-term and effective preventative for this is *exercise*. Exercise keeps the joints loose, improves muscle strength and function, permits oxygen to flow through the joints and thereby reduces pain and discomfort.

A few years ago, I had difficulty with parts of the dressing process. I experienced some difficulty bending over to tie my shoes. Sometimes I had excruciating pain putting on a coat, and I could not pull on or off an over-the-head garment — an undershirt, sweater, etc. without help and without experiencing extreme pain.

Today, a few years later and after much exercise and many hours of limb and muscle stretching, I have none of these problems.

Exercise isn't always easy. Many people shy away from exercise, not because they don't believe in it or want the benefit it brings, but primarily because it is *work*.

Exercise may be compared to a youngster growing up. There is an element of happiness and periods of great pleasure, but the *growing-up process* is at best frustrating, laborious and at times very difficult. The early years are probably the most difficult with all the learning, denials and limitations.

The middle years are better, but they also carry their share of frustrations and mixed emotions.

Adulthood and the later years often bring labor and sorrow heightened by hardship. *Life is always a struggle to some degree.*

We were made to reach, to climb, to press on, to persevere, to aspire and to strive. Should life ever lose these challenges, it will deteriorate to mere existence and to a point where it will not be worth living. *If life is worthless, so is the soul.*

So it is with exercise. In the beginning stages, the fixed and frozen muscles and joints are called on to flex and stretch. They physically rebel, and the result is pain and soreness. After this initial stage, the tenderness, soreness, pain and exhaustion lessen, but at no time is the exercising participant completely free from the hardships associated with exercise.

When I started an exercise program a few years ago, I started with a stretching routine. After a few turns, twists and reaches, I felt tired and the pain was excruciating. At first, I tried to jog around a long block. At the end of the four-block run, I was completely exhausted.

Whenever I tried to extend the distance, I could not run much farther. Discouraged, I shared with my doctor my slow progress and apparent inability to improve my run. He suggested that I run a few blocks, then walk a couple. He said the alternating would give me time to get my breath, while at the same time, train and condition my muscles and joints.

For weeks, I ran three blocks and walked two, three blocks and walked one. Then I ran six or seven blocks and walked two or three. After several weeks of daily perseverance, I delightfully discovered that I could run (or fast walk) eight to ten blocks without stopping. Although I could hardly get my breath, that condition also gradually improved, as did my strength, endurance and stamina. I now jog two miles three times a week and attend karate twice per week (where I obtained my black belt during the past four-year period) while carrying on other athletic and recreational activities.

My physical progress has been nothing short of phenomenal. I progressed from near exhaustion at the end of three blocks to near exhaustion at the end of six or seven blocks, to the end of eight or ten blocks, to the end of the first mile and then to the end of the second mile.

I am no longer exhausted at the end of the two-mile run. I used to have to rest before showering and would usually need more rest before beginning my day's duties. Now, I shower and proceed to the day's chores as usual. Rewards have manifested from the progression of these accomplishments.

Now, when I run the first half mile, I recall how my leg muscles used to tighten and physically cry out for release, how at the end of the first mile my breathing was laboriously short and my lungs and chest ached as I gasped for air that I could not inhale. I would stagger until my weak, trembling legs could gather enough strength to start me on the return trip.

Then came one of the most unexpectant, surprising, unbelievable experiences ever — the *"second wind"*! I always thought of second wind as that which came to distance runners, marathoners and only to younger people.

I have confidence and faith in myself, in human nature, in the future and in the Holder of the future,

God Himself. I am blessed and fortunate to be the re-recipient and beneficiary of these physical, mental, emotional and spiritual prowesses.

The *quest is costly!* It calls for *dedicated discipline, supreme sacrifice, undaunted determination and indubitable belief* and faith in yourself that not only can the goal of improved health and existence be accomplished through exercise and self-discipline, but that it is worth the sacrifice to accomplish it.

No Halfway Effort!

While it could be argued that any amount of exercise accrues some degree of body benefit, it is safe to say that maximum benefit comes only through *maximum input and self-dedication.*

Some people want to count kitchen work, making beds and a few trips up and down the stairs each day as exercise. It is indeed exercise, but in many cases, a far cry from the amount needed or the capability of the person. Depending upon the age, strength and general health of the individual, this may be adequate, while for another person, it would be totally inadequate and of little benefit. There isn't the continuous exertion that raises the heart rate above its normal pace for 15 minutes or more and which causes the muscles and tissues to stretch.

For maximum benefit, your exercise routine should include at least 15 minutes of activity (walking, jogging, swimming, etc.) which challenges the respiratory system and demands extended flexibility of muscles and joints.

To the hearty, healthy person who eats well, an adequate exercise program involves more than a walk around the block and a bit of toe or knee touching. Like all other worthwhile ventures, the body has to be driven to its highest performance, goals and achievement.

Some people are greatly disappointed when they exercise and little or no benefit results. I have observed people who all but starved themselves trying to lose weight, and they either held their own in weight or even gained.

In the first case, the exercise was too little, and in the second, the lack of exercise and the food intake accounted for the problem. You cannot take in 300 calories, burn only 40 and expect to control weight. After a time of indulging and over-indulging, large amounts of fat are stored in the body. This, too, must be burned off before maximum weight loss and exercise reward can be achieved.

Benefits of Exercise

The potential benefits and rewards of exercise are multitudinous, so numerous indeed that it is surprising why more older people don't discipline themselves to engage in it.

Proper exercise builds and tones muscles. As you grow older, the unused and little-used muscles sag and lose their rigidity and firmness, thereby causing a loss of strength. The result is a tiredness, even with the least exertion. It is depressing and exasperating to find yourself winded from a walk up one flight of stairs or after walking a block or two. The remedy or prevention to this dilemma is diligent exercise.

Proper exercise empowers the heart and lungs. The heart can experience enlargement from two primary conditions, one injurious, the other healthy.

Disease and overload of the heart can cause a negative enlargement, while regular exercise and in some cases even strenuous exercise, can enlarge the heart in a positive or healthy way. The heart becomes healthier and stronger. When the heart is stronger, the entire body benefits through maximum oxygenated blood flow.

Like a high-powered motor driving a compact car, the heart does not have to work hard but drives the body well while operating at a cruising pace.

The lungs also need expansion through proper exercise. They do their best work and develop maximum strength through regular, consistent exertion. Exercise causes the lungs to reach beyond the normal expansion point and pulls dormant tissues and blood vessels into maximum use.

The blood the heart pumps through the body picks up impurities and contaminants in the form of carbon dioxide gas. It is the function of the lungs to reclean the blood by removing the carbon dioxide, CO_2, and replacing it with fresh oxygen.

Better Sleep and Rest

Proper exercise is conducive to better sleep and rest habits.

When God created man, He gave specific examples as to ''how'' man should live. In Genesis 2:2, He said, **''And on the seventh day *God ended his work* which he had made; and he rested on the seventh day** *from all his work* **which he had made.''**

In Exodus 20:9,10, He said:

"Six days shalt thou labour, and *do all thy work:*

*"*But the seventh day is the sabbath of the Lord thy God: in it thou *shalt not do any work...."*

We need to practice God's instructions for rest and relaxation.

The body is designed for work and rest, and at its best requires a full measure of each. Anyone with reasonable knowledge knows what happens when you rest all the time. The body degenerates into a mass of flabby tissues, firmless and toneless muscles and a general weakened condition. It is equally well known that *"all work and no play"* not only make Jack a dull boy, but also make him an unsociable regimentarian with no real joy in life.

The heart and lungs work together, like the horse and carriage. No one feels more like working (recreating) than a person who has had a full measure of rest and relaxation. Nothing readies you more for sound and pleasant repose than a hard day's work.

Consistent Exercise Rejuvenates

Consistent exercise rejuvenates your faith in God, life itself, people and self.

Each person experiences both pleasant and unpleasant, happy and unhappy, good and bad circumstances. The pleasant, the happy and the good are welcome and easy to incorporate into the web of *life and living.* There is, however, a great need, especially on the part of the older person, to devise methods and practices to aid in coping with the bad, unpleasant and unhappy experiences.

The Psalmist David said, **"They go from strength to strength..."** (Psalm 84:7).

Life is a continuous struggle against the evil and negative powers that be. There must be an ongoing process of refreshing, refilling and rejuvenation if the spirit, body and soul are to remain strong and defensible in this moral war. Each victory helps us some other to *win*.

In all conditions of life, the spirit, soul and body strive together to bring us to meaning and fruition. Exercise, ordained of God for His creatures, is the hub around which much of the empowering of these three realms are geared. In this function, exercise joins hands with the *other-than-mundane* and flourishes in the realm of faith.

Exercise rejuvenates your faith in people. People come in three varieties: *good, bad and indifferent*. It is difficult to love the bad and tolerate the indifferent, along with the good. To do this, it helps if the body is in a healthy state. A person is then able to employ, to a maximum degree, the agents of the mind and spirit to see the good in the bad and to generate a heart of mercy and forgiveness toward the intolerable.

Proper, consistent exercise rejuvenates *faith in God*. Faith in God pervades the entire realm of life, and in the process, calls for the best in all of life. Sound faith emanates from healthy bodies, minds and spirits. *God is all and in all. You cannot believe in and commit to Him spiritually and not have your mental and physical life affected.* When a person is *made whole spiritually*, he immediately desires and seeks ways through which to bring the *mind and body into subjection to God.*

Through exercise, the mental capacities are sharpened. This provides the ability to consider, reflect and think on the ways and will of God and faith is embraced.

Proper exercise, even in your senior years, rejuvenates a proper love and respect for *yourself*. If there is no love for yourself, there is no love for others. If there is no trust in yourself, then there is no trust in others. If there is no faith in yourself, there will certainly be none in others.

Shoot for the Stars!

Despairing has never been known for victorious accomplishment. Persons who have sprinkled history with *remarkable feats, daring adventures* and *memorable achievements* have been those who *dared, persevered and determined.*

The older person must forget about or not allow the mind to dwell on age, years, weaknesses and inabilities, but rather concentrate on hope, opportunity and possibility. Armed with these, the older person becomes a *tower of strength, harnessed atoms* and *chained lightning.* The sky is just the first goal for those who dare and determine.

There are uncharted seas, an undiscovered world of worth and peerless pearls encased in the ore of the elderly all for the asking. It calls for those oldsters who believe they can be healthy, exercise, be happy, productive and do the *unexpected*, the *unbelievable* and the *impossible.* To do this, they must think young, dream big and aspire high.

It is my opinion that there are many older people who, given time, preparation and practice, could do most of the things they did when they were young. I believe there are those crippled with arthritis who could be doing two- and three-mile runs, that many who are bedfast should and could be doing their housework, shopping, etc., that thousands should be returning to school to complete their high school, college and doctoral studies, and that many who are dead could, with a proper concept of and approach to life, be alive and well today.

The suggestion unreservedly implied here is that there is a great waste accruing at the point of what has become fearfully known as old age. In far too many cases, talent, knowledge, ability, expertise, wisdom, counsel, strength and purpose are all thrown to the wind or written off under the banner of *old age.*

This phobia must be stopped! Younger people who want to see their loved ones live longer, be happier and live more useful lives and older people who desire the same must both join hands — in mind and effort — to hasten the dawning of *"a new day"* for older people.

10

The Interrelationship of Sex and Exercise

Until recently, whenever I read or heard that sex may be engaged in and enjoyed well into the later years of life — the 70s, 80s and upwards — I thought of it as perhaps simply an encouragement for wishful thinking. I also perceive, through observation and discussion, that this concept is shared by many.

Historically, sex has been linked with other physical and aging maladies. Accordingly, it has been "written off" for the older years. So ingrained and etched has it been upon the minds of many that there has been a great degree of psychological compromise in the sex arena for the older person.

This psychological compromise is the process of *giving in and giving up,* in many cases before nature *calls or cancels.* Just as many older persons decide that they can no longer *walk, run, hear, or think,* likewise, many decide prematurely that their sex lives have ended.

In the wake of new discoveries and treatments, coupled with better health and life-strengthening techniques, you owe it to yourself to explore the realms of *practicality, promise and possibility* in this area before calling it quits.

Body Exercise and Sex

As I presume is the case with most men, as the realization of the "season of diminish" of sexual prowess begins, I, too, entertained great concern. In sharing with my doctor, I recall him telling me something to which I had not given any thought. He said, "Keep your exercise up so that you will have the energy to perform."

A great amount of energy is required to perform the sex act. Herein lies the *jig-saw puzzle* of the interrelationship of the three main powers of the human entity and their ability or commonality to pull together in the interest of this great love act.

These three — body, mind and spirit — working together, transcend the common, the carnal and the conscious and provide for a realm of function above and beyond that of the ordinary.

Sex has been declared by some schools of thought to be purely mental (of the mind), and therefore, completely controlled by the mental faculties or state of concentration. Although it seems safe to suggest that perhaps the greater portion of students on this subject are enrolled in this *mental* school, there are those who place great worth and weight on the physical or the body's abilities.

For the older person especially, there is another dimension that is helpful, and that is the spiritual, which will be discussed later.

The Mind

There is little question that the mind plays a special role in the act of sexual encounter. It is commonly known that the agents of sexual impedance — *doubt, self-criticism and fear,* among others — greatly handicap the capacity to perform.

Generally, the body does whatever the mind instructs the brain to tell it to do (within its physical realm of ability). Hence, it is reasonable to say:

If you think you can,
You likely will,
But if you think you can't,
You probably won't.

As great as the mind power is, the will power is strongly affected and influenced by another power factor, the physical.

For maximum performance in any area of life and life's endeavors, the three-fold power pact — *physical, mental* and *spiritual* — must be interrelated, synchronized and harmonized. If any one area is out of sync or is functioning below par, the other two areas are equally and proportionately limited. The common mistake many make is attempting to separate these three areas or to employ one or two in absence of the others, and then wonder why true success and satisfaction are not achieved.

To express it in another way, the human creation was made a "tri-product," and one area cannot excel without the support and contribution of the other two.

Although it is true that sex is more than a simple physical operation, it is also more than a motion from the mind. There must be physical powers. This ability comes from input from the other two powers, which call the body system into the discipline of good habits, conduct and practices. One of these is the practice and habit of exercise.

Exercise

As stated elsewhere in this book, the Creator of the body designed it for *work, recreation* and *play,* which serve the same purpose for the good of the body. Work at its best is that which is made recreation or play, in a loose sense, and makes that which would be drudgery pleasant and enjoyable.

Since the body is designed for work action, it cannot develop to its fullest physical potential without work and exercise, and since the sexual act requires physical strength, it follows that exercise is essential. Exercise is a *power source for sexual prowess.*

The Spiritual Aspect of Sex

The mind may be distracted by matter or the body by fatigue, but the spiritual remains true to itself and its cause. It is this source of power and energy that enables the other body sisters when they falter.

This spiritual dimension aids the total person through continuous loyalty and calls to principles and truths, which make for love's longevity: *cleanliness, honesty and devotion of:* the mind; purity, commitment and dedication of the physical body; and sincerity and submission to the spiritual.

While the older person would do well to expect and prepare to accept a progressive diminishing of sexual powers, there is no reason to despair. Life does not begin at forty, nor does it necessarily end at ninety. Some people enjoy a greater sex life after the 50s and 60s than before. Some have greater sexual ability during the 60s, 70s and 80s than others have in early adulthood.

Although there are extenuating circumstances in some cases and while individuals are different, an assimilation of the *trinity towers of power* — *body, mind and spirit* — will prove that the divine plan, made for mankind, if not dishallowed, cannot be destroyed.

There's a lot of truth to the following poem, even in relationship to the sexual fulfillment of the aging person.

The body, mind and spirit true;
Make greater souls than we would be,
But only when in time,
We grow to honor them stronger than we.

11
Loving Others

More miracles are wrought by love than by power!

It is impossible to live a truly happy, meaningful and useful life without a spirit of love for others. The great wonder for many people is why, after much labor, living and giving, they are still unhappy, their lives are empty and their efforts are unrewarded. More often than not, the reason lies at the very doorstep of their existence, undetectable to them, the *absence of love*.

Love is among the strongest elements of life, if not the strongest. Whatever is not of love does not have the sanction of the *Super Force* of the universe. Failure to have God's endorsement relegates these unlovely acts, thoughts, words and deeds to the heap of unprofitableness where maximum good in all human endeavor is critically minimized. Those who fail or refuse to love cheat themselves out of full life, at the same time robbing the unloved of their most precious aspiration and right.

It is said that there are three types of givers: the *flint*, the *lemon* and the *honeycomb*. The flint giver is one who, like flint, gives only what is hammered off or out. The lemon giver has to be squeezed. But the honeycomb giver just *gives* and *gives freely* and *generously*.

True love falls in the latter category. True love does not ask *how much*. It does not *seek or wait for praise*, because it is always seeking additional ways to give. Love gives and gives, never counting the cost or requiring reciprocation.

Love and the Echo

Love is like the echo — the more that is sent out, the more comes back. The louder the voice sent into the echo area, the louder the return voice.

Love doesn't always come from the object loved, but finds sources and expressions both foreign and unknown to the natural persons. All this is made eternally essential in the fact that the Lover does not require, expect, or wish this plus return.

Love rewards its bearer in direct proportion to higher *selflessness, single-mindedness and sincerity*. It is impossible to love without being loved. Love moves the world. It is reflected in the spring season, when Life dances on the surface of the green. It revives and re-utilizes the hearts of those who bear and need love. It is registered in the summer's sun, warming the soul in its sacred world as the sun warms the earth. It is exhibited in the annals of autumn, preparing the object of its affection for the coming storms and uneven weather that tries men's souls. It sustains the bleakness of wintertime when frigidness tempts all to turn cold.

The echo calls back each whisper of love and magnifies its depth, worth and volume by a thousand gifts.

The Roller Coaster Syndrome

Philosophically speaking, love, like the roller coaster, is a several-sided, multi-faceted, many-splendored thing. It serves many purposes, fills many needs, causes many changes, takes many stands, suffers many pains, walks many miles and savors many triumphs.

The roller coaster runs, yet it stays. It leaves, yet it returns to the exact spot it left. It runs at great speeds, yet remains on track. It traverses uphill and down, round and round, sometimes looping itself without losing control.

Few entities go through as many changes as love does. The love and the loved go from pillar to post, doormat to door, pinnacle to valley, victory to victimization and ecstasy to agony. But like the roller coaster, it is involved in *doing*. It never *rests*, *sleeps*, or *despairs*. It works toward *union* and *reunion*. It *encourages, enables, enlightens*. It *creates, comforts, controls, concedes, concertizes, condoles, conserves and consummates*. It makes life *worth living*, gives meaning to *existence*, engendering *faith*, heightening *hope*, drying tears of sorrow, breeding tears of joy, breaking down barriers and equalizing all.

It *suffers* even as it *protects from suffering*, it *hurts* as it *caresses*, it is attached as it *defends* and it *stands alone*, even as it *mates, binds, births* and opens the gates of bliss to all who trust, believe and persevere.

Loving Everyone

Love has no bounds, sanctions purity and courts perfection. Although it does not require perfection on the part of its adherents, it does call them to recognition of appreciation for and progression toward these eternal verities.

Love refuses to be judged by any standard other than its own. It needs none, because of its all-inclusive, nonsectarian nature. Although one may legitimately love another with greater passion, feeling or intensity, one cannot love another for any greater reason than the other. The reason, the purpose and the motivation must be the same for all.

When these entities are disregarded or neglected, you can practice the art of loving in a discriminating, biased and selfish manner. This is what happens when you love on the basis of class, color, or station in life. In these instances, the full benefits and blessing of love are not experienced by those who are the object of love nor of those called on to love.

The immensity and the eternality of love demand more than a mere feeling or a good wish from one toward another in the world community. If humanity is anything, it is more than race, class, or kind. It is *family*, it is *bone of bone, flesh of flesh, heart of heart* and *of the Spirit*.

If a member of a family has trouble loving another member, higher blood sisters and brothers, it is not the fault of the family. It isn't that the person wasn't properly brought into the family. It isn't that the other unloved member of the family is unlovable. It is that the person who finds difficulty loving the other violates the principles of love and thereby renders himself ineligible for the full blessings of loving or being loved.

Those who fall victim to these enemies of love usually become *mean, inconsiderate* and *intolerable*. When love is cheated, it does not leave the area, the object, or the purpose of the one who refuses to embrace it, but waits outside, retires from the heart of the recalcitrant one for invitation to residence. Whoever does not love all does not truly love any. Herein is the tragedy of love, for all are cheated and the cause of love is thwarted.

We were created by Love, and the constraining incentive for creating was love. Whoever, then, does not love the Creator, and himself, renders himself incapable of loving others or incapable of appropriate self-love.

Jesus set forth an eternal moral principle in Mark 12:33 — **"...and to love his neighbour as himself...."** Loving God fully, which is the first commandment, sets the stage for loving others.

A neighbor may not only be someone who lives near another geographically or socially, but may be, in a deeper sense, someone who lives close to the heart. Ordinarily, a person doesn't choose his neighbors. They just move in. They are nonetheless neighbors, and it is a person's social responsibility to treat them as such.

You do not have to always be in a neighbor's house, drive the same kind of car, or paint your house the same color to be a good neighbor. It is equally true that you don't have the freedom or the right to choose your neighbors.

Likewise, we don't have to run with another person, always agree with them, or condone their conduct to be a neighbor or to love them.

Love transcends status, rank, national origin, or station in life. It brings all to a common denominator — *caring*. When you truly care, you *care for all, bear all and treat all equally.*

All is all there is,
Anything less is naught.
One's gift to another is his,
Or what has anyone wrought?

Love and Religion

Love refuses to be bound by a religious affiliation. Religion is a code of conduct by which you are governed and a way of life in recognition of and loyalty to a deity. Love is so essential that deity, at its best, is to be equated with love. Deity at its best is love.

Love cares to the extent that it has to have a personal epitome. It is fundamental to existence and so *essential to all things* that it *defies definition*. It escapes the confines of nationality and takes its abode in the clime of *all*.

There are sundry types, forms and degrees of religion, each determining the *"Code of Conduct"* for its disciples. Not so with love. Love has one *stand* and one *approach*, one *method*, one *format*, one *motivation*, one *inspiration* and one *sentimentality*. This all-inclusive code of conduct gives no quarters or consideration to *age, rank, color, creed, class, cast, national origin, or religious alignment.*

A religion might allow or provide for separation or discrimination based on *lack* or *plenty, social status,* or *religious rank.*

Love *sees, regards, holds* and *demands* equity for all. *Love is more than sentimentality* and exceeds all mundane boundaries. It defies personal preferences and prejudices. Yet, it is fair and impartial in its requirements. Love does not require that you embrace the negative things that it does not endorse — *prejudice, ill will, bias, hate,* etc.

According to the principle of love, one may object to a neighbor on the basis of *manifested misconduct*, but not on the basis of the above negatives. One may object to a new neighbor because he is a dope pusher or a child molester, but one may not object because he is Indian or Hispanic, because he wears his hair long, or he isn't a church goer.

Love recognizes shortcomings, excuses those who are faultless, but holds accountable those who are not. *Love flourishes*, even where *religion fails*. It questions, philosophizes and dares dogmas.

If religion does not demand fair play, justice and mercy, then love does. If religion fails to hear or heed the cries of the hungry, the suffering and those left out, love lingers with them. Love may not always be able to supply the physical, societal, or cultural needs, but it is always present, *lifting, upholding, supporting, sustaining, endearing, comforting, challenging, breaking, mending, reminding, warming and initiating.*

The Good Samaritan was not able to choose his neighbor; he just came upon him. Had the injured man had the comfort of choice, he may well have chosen the priest or the Levite. Oh, the difference in toil, tolerance, sacrifice and cost! The Good Samaritan could have passed the man by with the excuse that he was *too dirty, too heavy, too costly,* or blamed him for getting himself in such a fix, but these excuses would not have been acceptable!

The Good Samaritan used his energy to pick the man up, he used his oil and wine for cleaning and reviving the victim (his neighbor), he used his credit card and then his money to pay the bill! The Good Samaritan was a true *neighbor.*

Love and Hate

Love is not simply the opposite of hate. It exceeds and transcends the opposite of hate. Love and hate do not have their existence in the same climate. Hate breeds the things that *hurt, wound, separate, destroy and kill,* while love's abode is on higher ground.

Love is where *caring, healing, binding, building,* and *making alive* exist and where the essence and glory of these prevail.

Love is forever and eternal. It is *light* and *life.* It is *indestructible, undefeatable, indefensible and indefatigable.* From time immemorial to eternity, love reigns supreme.

The universe and the beyond are held together by a good Spirit — the Holy Spirit. Comfort is coveted over pain, happiness is heralded over sadness, joy is enjoined against sorrow and goodness is elevated over evil.

If there had never been a Bible, a book on ethics, never a sermon preached or a lesson taught on morality, there would still have existed within the heart of humanity the desire and preference to be helped rather than hurt, to be accepted rather than rejected and to be loved rather than hated. The intelligence of all creation sides with *love.* Only the lower instincts of nature give in to hate.

It was so at the beginning of the Christian age. As Jesus taught the way of love, He said:

> "Ye have heard that it hath been said, Thou shalt love thy neighbour, and hate thine enemy.
>
> "But I say unto you, Love your enemies, bless them that curse you, do good to them that hate you, and pray for them which despitefully use you, and persecute you."
>
> **Matthew 5:43,44**

Under the law, it is permissible for a moral person to love a friend, a good neighbor, any acceptable person of like *conduct, preference, race, color and ethnicity.* The law made it lawful to *discriminate, disassociate, segregate and relegate.* According to the law of love, it is unlawful to withhold love for any cause.

Jesus set a love standard that *benefits both neighbors.* The admonition to love your enemies evokes a great challenge upon the person who must make the decision to love or hate. He can diminish both by hating, or bless both by loving.

On the surface, it appears that this call to love enemies is all to the benefit of the enemy. Not so! It is equally to the benefit of the person so challenged. The question which prevails is, "What are you going to do if you *don't* love your enemies?" Hate them? If this is done, the chance to improve this *status, standard and quality* of life is lost forever. The hater loses more than the hated, because he had the greater opportunity.

We are made of *strange stuff:* the good of God and the debris of the devil. We can love immensely or hate with fury. We can wish well or desire disastrous evil on others. We are fully capable of speaking words of cheer or spewing poisonous verbal darts of *discord, confusion and consternation.*

Twelve Facts About Love

1. Love exceeds the wrath of God.

2. More good will is wrought by love than by language.

3. More good will is wrought by love than by prayer.

4. Love is never advanced in its own interest.

5. One is not bound to acquiesce to another's conduct in order to love.

6. Love is never limited to nor bound by the physical.

7. It is impossible to love without a spiritual motivation.

8. There is but one true love. All else must be known by other names.

9. One can love, yet not desire another's presence.

10. Love does not attempt to love equally — only completely.

Love Is Not...

1. Purposeless acquiescence.

2. Condoning carelessness.

3. Willing weakness.

4. Selfishly motivated.

5. A substitute for reality.

6. An excuse for reality.

7. Fear of the truth.

8. Calloused or color blind.

9. The opposite of hate.

10. Pity but penance.

11. Secret sentimentality.

12. Softness and insensitivity.

13. Rejecting responsibility.
14. Responding irresponsibly.

Love Is...

1. Concern in action.
2. The heart's response to a human need.
3. Remembering never to forget.
4. Heaven's response to earth's needs.
5. Forgetting to remember the bad.
6. Giving a hand where a hand cannot give.
7. Mixing day with night.
8. Hurting for another.
9. Mixing light with darkness.
10. Providing sunlight on a rainy day.
11. Religion in action.
12. Care addressed.
13. Sympathy activated.
14. Acting responsibly.
15. Being one's best.
16. Generating care.
17. Caring creatively.
18. Valuing worth.
19. A picture of one's self reflected in another.
20. Tenderness transmitted.
21. A tear for another's eye.
22. A walk through the forest without fear.
23. The epitome of existence.

24.   Doing good unreservedly.

25.   Being to others what they can't be to themselves.

26.   Looking past sight.

27.   Seeing what is not shown.

28.   Looking beyond people to possibility.

29.   Not being color conscious.

30.   Being bigger than....

31.   A season of sobriety.

32.   Spawning responsibility.

33.   Remembering to remember the good.

12

Agape Love

The climax, the bottom line, the last word of love is to be found in 1 Corinthians 13. Paul's love letter states what love is and what it is not, how it behaves and what can be expected of it; the immediacy, the eternality, the glory, wisdom, tenderness, commonality, unselfishness and the excellency of it.

In this love letter, Paul writes to the Corinthians out of a heart of love, a love motivated by and magnified in the great love of God, which he had come to realize and lay hold of. It was a precious, immeasurable love. It was a love for sinners! (The mind has to stretch its imagination and extend its comprehension to conceive of such a passion.) It was a love for sinners, of which Paul considered himself the greatest.

It had to be the *greatest love,* since it was full and complete for any person who was diametrically different, wantonly unworthy and duly undeserving. It was a love that would cover and include a transgressor to the will and way of the Maker.

For Paul, no love could be greater, no love could match the prompting to proclaim that it is a selfless, single, satisfying love. It was before the foundation of the world. It is an *anticipated love.*

This love seeks all. Therefore, each finder becomes a seeker of others. Love is undefeated, for even in refusal and rejection, love triumphs in *anticipation, communication and expectation.* There is no waste, for acceptance is in full measure, and all sharing fulfills the plan of love.

The case of love is made,
How can one deny?
The heart throb of the universe displays,
To give us lodging in the sky.

In this love chapter, Paul summarizes all that he would ever say about love. I have attempted to emphasize that love is the undergirding force of the universe of humanity and existence. Without it, we would not only be *empty, useless* and *void,* but we would be without *value* and *purpose.*

Paul states the case for love. With it, *all win.* Without it, *all lose.* With it, life is *meaningful.* Without it, *meaningless.* With it, the rich and the poor are rich together.

Love and Languages

"Though I speak with the tongues of men and
of angels, and have not charity, I am become as
sounding brass, or a tinkling cymbal."
1 Corinthians 13:1

Love exceeds all barriers and excels all excellence. It is not bound by the senses or the intellect. Dialects differ and tongues twist, but love has only one message — universally and completely comprehensible. The damsel and the suitor may speak in different tongues, but their hearts will beat as one. The heart does not have to know the language of the head in order to beat with truth. Indeed, the head may say "yes" when the answer is "no," or "no" when the answer is really "yes."

No tongue or language can increase or enhance love. All else is enhanced by love. As important and as urgent as the languages are — for communication, progress and understanding — they are void and empty without love. For love is the queen of the universe and reigns supreme!

What strange things love,
Yet in that strangeness,
Truth enters from above
And worlds are changed.

Love and Gifts

The gift of prophecy, mastery of all mysteries, all knowledge, all faith and the ability to remove mountains — who wouldn't settle happily for just one of these? To be able to foretell and predict that which is to come, unravel, interpret and explain all the things which baffle and mystify others...to have all the answers and know the dark secrets...to possess a mastery of faith so that one is not plagued with human and natural doubt and to have all earthly power...what more can the heart desire? What else is there? The answer is, LOVE.

As phenomenal, as extraordinary and as eternally associated as these entities are, they all depend on and have their worth in LOVE.

Let prophecy have its day in the court of world affairs. Let prophets ring out messages of cheer and doom. Let the masters of mysteries exploit their genius and mystify their procurement of deep unknowns to the common person. Let knowledge flourish in her finest hour, lifting minds to heights undreamed of.

Let faith find favor with the future. Let her demonstrate time and time again that it is more profitable to walk with her than with her sister, "sight." Let ability shine forth as the noonday sun, *win all wars, conquer all foes, vanquish all enemies and subdue all undesirable powers* that be.

But the Kingdom will not come, the lions will not lay down with the lambs, the beasts of the wild will not be led by little children, there will be no peace on earth nor good will toward humanity. Nations will never beat their swords into plowshares nor their spears into pruninghooks.

The world will not be bettered, nor the lives of those who live, until love has been given the head seat at the conference table of human affairs and her soft voice and touch have been heard, felt and responded to.

Love's Continuity

"Let brotherly love continue" (Hebrews 13:1).

To love is honorable. To work for its lively progression is holy. The peace of life and coexistence is sometimes broken, not only by the failure to love, but by carelessness in human relations. An unkind deed is done, an unfitting word is spoken in haste, an uncaring attitude breaks a heart and love's work is hindered, its stride shortened and its sunlight dimmed, prompting Paul to exhort, **"Let brotherly love continue."**

One inference I have gleaned is that love, left on its own, will serve all needs, cover all faults, fill all emptiness and pay all debts. It is only when love meets opposition from a teammate that it is handicapped. Love says, as it were, "If you aren't going, don't hinder me. If you are not on my side, don't be against me. If you aren't with me, leave me alone. Let me do my own thing."

Love is best expressed as Christian, love has its origin in God, and God, in His effort to commute that love to His perishing human creations, chose His own only begotten Son as the channel. This love, coming forth from a perfect God, was perfectly executed by Him and perfectly manifested by the Son, Jesus Christ.

This love then has its greatest impact and results when communicated in the name, honor, manner and Spirit of the One who perfectly loved us first.

Eros and phileo love, as opposed to agape (or Christlike love), can be selfish and discriminating. This kind of love can be turned on and off at will according to conditions. Not so with *agape love!* The God-kind of love — agape love — loves unconditionally, unstintingly and in spite of.

It is *futile, confusing* and *frustrating* to attempt to love with your own personal ability. The old hymn says it so well, "Ask the Savior to help you, comfort, strengthen and keep you; He is willing to help you. He will carry you through."

Love and Religion

Any religion that is not rooted in love is *empty, cruel* and *unyielding.* Such a religion could never be potent, effective and useful because it is the opposite of fulfilling sympathy and a self-giving faith that make for *a religion of love.*

Religion has its basic purpose in the teaching, implementation and perfection of a *code of conduct, method* and *manner of living*. It brings to every person involved in it the good life of faith, friendship and fellowship, which gears the person for full, useful and rewarding living in the present and provides a dress rehearsal for the life to come.

In order to serve its role well, religion then, must challenge, call for and divinely demand a love-centered association.

Religion helps love in its quest, and love helps religion. To be without religion, love would be minus one of its strongest advocates, and without love, religion would be powerless and meaningless. Wherever love finds its expression difficult, it calls on religion to defend the meeting of the spiritual and the mental or natural (the heart and the head).

The definition of religion persuades the whole of humanity — neighborliness, marriage, business, play, courtship, etc. with a "Thou-shalt-care-about-the-other-person" ethic. Those who profess and foster this definition find a bonding force of love and religion as they practice it.

Love Says What the Bible Does Not

The Bible tells *what* and *who* God is. Love strives to go the *"love mile"* further and point out *"how"* God is. The Bible says, "God is love." Love says there is a depth to itself. If God is love, then love is God. This is why love is *everlasting, eternal, ongoing* and *self-sustaining*.

God doesn't just love. He loves *especially, specifically, particularly, completely, sufficiently* and in a way that no one else can. *"So loved"* is *how* He loved.

It is a *degreeless* love, and it cannot be *measured, explained* or *contained.*

It is:

* God's kind of love.

* God's way of loving.

* God's unmatched love.

* God's redeeming love.

* God's sufficient love.

* God's perfect love.

* God's *anticipated love.*

In growing old gracefully, regardless of your present age, I am emphasizing the importance of agape love, because it will always solve the challenges you face in relationships, in provision, in protection, in care and in knowing how to react to others and love them as God would have you.

God So Loved

In an effort to express the greatness and completeness of God's love for His most particular and precious creation — mankind — John, the beloved brother and disciple, declares, *"God so loved."*

> "For *God so loved* the world, that he gave his only begotten Son, that whosoever believeth in him should not perish, but have everlasting life."
>
> **John 3:16**

God's kind of love infers an *orderly, timely, meaningful* and *lasting* kind of love. God loves in a way that never needs *repeating, upgrading,* or *improving.* God invests so much of Himself in the love venture that any subject or creature of the Creator can, by choice, become enough like the Creator to have full fellowship with Him, and as a result, share His kind of love with others.

Mutually Enjoined

Love is *people-centered* and is humanistically inclined. It is at its best when Jesus calls on His followers to *love one another.*

> "This is my commandment, That ye love one another, as I have loved you.
>
> "These things I command you, that ye love one another."
>
> John 15:12,17

While Jesus speaks more directly to His disciples, it is clear that He includes all of humanity in His *love pattern.* He calls on us to love the world of people so much that we will seek them out, inform them about Him and bring them under His umbrella of love where they become His disciples, and at a point, all of society will form the love triangle.

People are the special species of the earth. There is no other species as *precious*, *prized* and *particular* to either God or man as humanity. Therefore, all of us, including older people, are challenged to *embrace*, *nurture* and *extend* a commonality and a reciprocity of love.

People Vs. Things

"**Lovest thou me?**" Jesus asked three times of Peter (John 21:15-17). These familiar words embody one of the most *profound*, *significant* and *far-reaching* questions of the Lord Jesus Christ during His earthly ministry.

This is so because it tends to differentiate between *"things"* and *created people.* God made *"things"* to serve the needs of His *higher creation* — *people.* He made *humanity* for His *glory,* for His honor and for *fellowship,* prompting the Psalmist to pose the question, **"What is man, that thou art mindful of him? and the son of man, that thou visitest him?"** (Psalm 8:4).

In the beginning of time, the Bible says that God came down in the cool of the evening for the express purpose of fellowshipping (communing) with mankind.

These two Biblical passages reflect God's immeasurable love for His human creations. He *cares* about "things" in the sense that they are the products of His hands and a part of His world; but He *loves* His human creatures because they are not only a creation of His hand, *they are part of Him!*

Self-love is not necessarily selfish. It is impossible to love another person without love for yourself. God's love is first for Himself, because love is *who He is* and *what He is.* He did not need to put forth effort to love mankind, and He did not need to generate a reason. *He was that reason.* Hence, the explanation, *"God so loved."*

The Andrew D. Phillips translation of **"Lovest thou Me?"** is: "Peter, have you caught on to the greatest force in the universe? Peter, do you have life's priorities straight? Peter, are you now clear on the difference of value between 'things' and people?"

Peter could like the fish for food, for income, for whatever advantage they afforded him, but his love was to be reserved for a higher purpose.

It is equally so with us. Love, the most precious commodity bestowed upon mankind, *must not be wasted!* It must be generously conferred upon all who are created in God's image, upon all who are capable of *appreciation* and *reciprocation*.

One must not attempt to love until there is a desire *to love fully*. Love comes in one *form* and *one package* — FULL — and it is to be dispersed in one portion — MUCH!

Wherever we are told of God's love, it is to a *generous, full, sufficient* and *complete* degree. Our love then, whether it be *fraternal, social, marital, family,* or *religious,* must be without *self-seeking, usurpation,* or *hypocrisy.* It must be full of godliness and good will for others. It is only then that we are ready and able to answer in our hearts the interrogation of the Lord Jesus as He repeats His question to Peter.

Love challenged Paul to never think that he had apprehended or measured up.

> "Brethren, I count not myself to have apprehended: but this one thing I do, forgetting those things which are behind, and reaching forth unto those things which are before,
>
> "I press toward the mark for the prize of the high calling of God in Christ Jesus."
> Philippians 3:13,14

Love calls forth the best in us for others. It is deeper than *the depths,* wider than *the world* and higher than *the heaven.* It is not something that you attain unto. It cannot be *mastered, measured* or *contained.* We are called to strive to enter in at the straight gate of love for others, to work at acquiring some reasonable, decent and satisfactory level of love of which we can be proud, others can be convinced and God can be pleased.

There is no earthly *graduation day, time of celebration,* or *relaxation.* You must always be *pressing, pursuing* and *improving,* reaching forth toward the ultimate degree of love.

Although there is no earthly *commencement* in the sense of *completion* or *perfection,* there is the *correspondence course* offered by the Supreme Love, which qualifies you for graduation and likeness to Him, beginning in this life and fully consummated when we step into His presence. **"...We shall be like him..."** (1 John 3:2).

Ableness

As stated earlier, some people are lovable, yet difficult to love. We are enjoined and given the impossible task of loving our enemies! Paul made the amazing discovery that this "impossibility" really has human possibility! It is within our grasp!

The human, mental, or sensual can never accomplish this task by itself. There must be outside, *greater-than,* or *other-than* help. Like Paul, we should believe, **"I can do all things through Christ which strengtheneth me"** (Philippians 4:13). Or like John said in His first epistle, **"...greater is he** [Jesus Christ] **that is in you, than he** [the devil] **that is in the world"** (1 John 4:4).

The *power, desire, strength* and *ability* to love your enemies (and sometimes your friends!) come from a Source beyond yourself. However, with this support and empowerment, it is not only accomplishable, but it is *positively profitable* and rewarding to all persons involved.

I have been blessed to have experienced this *unbelievable transformation.* All my life I have struggled with the difficulty of loving many people and the inability to love my enemies.

For Paul, ableness to love effectively came from a Source outside and greater than himself. So it is with us. I may sincerely want to love others, and even try to love them, but sometimes *attitudes, personalities characteristics, weaknesses* and *shortcomings* make it difficult to do so. To love an enemy who openly persecutes and antagonizes borders on the impossible. Paul then observes that it can be done — with extra help — *through Christ!*

Call it what you will, the fact remains, we humans, to become our best, must lay claim to and establish a relationship with a power outside of ourselves. A great portion of today's society ascribes this power only to the God of the universe. I am numbered among this group.

Love Vs. Things

"Love is very patient and kind, never jealous or envious, never boastful or proud,

"Never haughty or selfish or rude. Love does not demand its own way. It is not irritable or touchy. It does not hold grudges and will hardly even notice when others do it wrong.

"It is never glad about injustice, but rejoices whenever truth wins out.

"If you love someone you will be loyal to him no matter what the cost. You will always believe in him, always expect the best of him, and always stand your ground in defending him.

"All the special gifts and powers from God will someday come to an end, but love goes on forever. Someday prophecy, and speaking in unknown languages, and special knowledge — these gifts will disappear.

"Now we know so little, even with our special gifts, and the preaching of those most gifted is still so poor.

"But when we have been made perfect and complete, then the need for these inadequate special gifts will come to an end, and they will disappear.

"It's like this: when I was a child I spoke and thought and reasoned as a child does. But when I became a man my thoughts grew far beyond those of my childhood, and now I have put away the childish things.

"In the same way, we can see and understand only a little about God now, as if we were peering at his reflection in a poor mirror; but someday we are going to see his completeness, face to face. Now all that I know is hazy and blurred, but then I will see everything clearly, just as clearly as God sees into my heart right now."

1 Corinthians 13:4-12 (TLB)

We live our lives as a tale that is told — man born of woman. We spend our years as a tale that is told — for it is soon cut off and we fly away. There is and always has been this great disparity between the present and the future, the now and the then, the here and the there, the immediate and the hereafter, time and eternity.

There has to be a Source of power that spans the eternal gap. That Source would have to be *all-encompassing,* full of *sympathy* and *empathy* and possess a *sacrificial self-giving Spirit* that encompasses the *entire scope of humanity's need.* Short of bringing God down from heaven or keeping His Son here on earth, there is but one other person! LOVE! Love fills the bill! We experience that love through the ever-present Holy Spirit.

The world rushes onward, temperance wears thin, friendships cannot withstand too many mistakes, even though they may be innocent mistakes.

In the midst of this, love stands *challenged but unchanged, unmoved, victimized* but not *vanquished*. Love fills the requirements. It can and will do what no other can or will do. It will wait without becoming impatient or feeling that too much is being asked of it. It has the tenderness of care to promote its subject, humanity.

Love defies definition. It cannot be analyzed. It is to be *pursued, purchased* and *practiced*. Paul does not attempt to define love. He chooses rather to more profitably explain what love does, why it does it and how.

Love will not become angry when it is mistreated, lose interest or patience, envy another's success or ability, but will keep on loving for love's sake and for the good of the other person.

How does one approximate this high standard of love? How does one ascend the holy hill of accomplishment? It is imperative that we become part of the fellowship of believers. This makes us God-like or Christ-like, and since God is love, we acquire the attainable attributes of God.

God suffers long, His patience is inexhaustible. He is kind beyond measure and gave Himself in the form of His Son for us.

Love and Behavior

While it is thought by many that Paul refers to worship and communion conduct in 1 Corinthians 13, it is implicit that he alludes to a wider berth of love conduct — our behavior in the arena of life.

There cannot be a double standard of conduct in behavior. There must not be a *Sunday* and a *week-day* conduct. Too many professing saints feel that a couple of hours spent in a church on Sunday negates the past week's transgressions.

It has been said that manners make the man. Manners, like thoughts, expose us for what we really are. We may try to impress, but the real "us" will eventually be revealed. Manners reveal not only what we think but what we believe and how strongly we believe.

Show me his manners,
And I will quote you the man.

This is a *structured, controlled* and *disciplined* love. It is not careless of the feelings of others, doesn't think only of itself, does not carry a chip on its shoulder and controls its thoughts so it doesn't get ahead of truth and reality. Above all else, it watches its behavior or manners. Love cannot and must not afford to *misrepresent, deceive,* or *mislead.* It watches its step and guards its tongue. Love never behaves unbecomingly and avoids arrogance and rudeness.

While love will not compromise its *principles, disregard truth,* or *give up* on its own, it is not mean or childish. It does not have to *have its own way.* It will not *throw a tantrum,* take its marbles and go home when something goes contrary to its wishes!

The Joy of Love

Because of the stuff of which we are made, there is a natural tendency to take a certain delight in getting away with wrongdoing and in seeing the *"reward of the wicked"* come on those who have done wrong — especially us! Not so with love. Love loves — regardless of *conditions, plight* or *state of existence.* Love *supports, bears up* and *wishes well,* even for those who appear to be unworthy.

Love is a mother figure. All humanity is her children. Some are *good, obedient* and *lovable;* others are *rebellious, wayward* and *unlovable.* But she *claims, embraces* and *loves them equally.* She does not love them for what they could or should be or for what they may become, but she loves just for love's sake. She is able to do this because it is her nature to be positive, to find happiness in the good of people, to ignore the false faith by putting on the full armor of truth.

Right doing is conduct sublime,
But truth is the bottom line.

Another fallacy common among those practicing Christian faith is the tendency and temptation to measure or grade themselves by the lowest standard or example available. Put another way, the more reprehensible the lives and conduct of those about them, the more righteous or saintly they feel. Not so with love. Love's greatest joy is in *enabling, enlightening* and *engaging* others.

Love cannot afford to pass on *unkind gossip, malicious slander,* or *wrongdoing.* Neither can it enjoy hearing about these negatives. It must ever wait for the passion of falsehood to pass and the thermometer of truth to be read.

Love depends on and trusts truth, because truth, like love, is self-contained and self-sustaining. Like love, truth does not wait to follow, but it leads. It does not determine its actions by the decisions of another but, in the face of whatever odds, danger, or persecution, it stands.

Love and Sacrifice

Giving is living. It has been so from the beginning. God gave the earth and all its contents to the use of humanity. Then *when nothing else could help,* He gave His only begotten Son. We are challenged by His Son to:

> "Give, and it shall be given unto you; good measure, pressed down, and shaken together, and running over, shall men give into your bosom. For with the same measure that ye mete withal it shall be measured to you again."
>
> **Luke 6:38**

And, **"...It is more blessed to give than to receive"** (Acts 20:35). These words of Jesus emphasize the blessings and rewards of giving.

There is, however, one unnamed ingredient which was with God in the beginning and which must accompany and prompt our giving. That ingredient is LOVE.

The spirit of benevolence is a wonderful characteristic to possess. The motive of giving must be pure. Whatever is done for *pride* or *self-glorification* is of little consequence.

The essence and endlessness of love are emphasized. Can more than all one has be required? Isn't *self-sacrifice sufficient?* The answer is a resounding, *not if it isn't motivated by love!*

A poet has well said, "Not what we give, but what we share, the gift without the giver is bare." The recipient may be blessed through a selfish gift, but the giver's blessing and reward hinges on proper motivation. The motivation which crowns the gift with eternal value and unseen riches is LOVE!

Love costs! The cost is *great* and *continuous.* Sometimes the cost is so enormous that the perpetrator

or wrongdoer learns that *you can't do wrong and get by.*
"For the wages of sin is death..." (Romans 6:23).
"...The soul that sinneth, it shall die" (Ezekiel 18:4).

There are other times, however, when the
wrongdoer not only seems to be void of learning, but
doesn't show any remorse for the misdeed. This is
when love bears the *full blame* and carries the *whole load.*

In my earlier years, the men back home had a
saying that related to friendships which articulates this
ideal very well. They said, "I am with you all the way.
I am with you when you are right to keep you right,
and I am with you when you are wrong to get you
right." That is the position love takes.

> **"If you love someone you will be loyal to him
> no matter what the cost. You will always believe in
> him, always expect the best of him, and always stand
> your ground in defending him."**
> **1 Corinthians 13:7 (TLB)**

Agape love, according to Verse 7 in the *King James
Version* of the Bible, ***"Beareth all things*, believeth all
things, hopeth all things, endureth all things."**

Oh, for the relationship in which no one *accuses*
or *seeks who is to blame!* Friendship seeks rewards, sets
boundaries, wears thin with abuse and seeks its own
in crisis.

Fraternities and sororities pledge faithfulness and
devotion, but sometimes renege on their promises
because of the overt misconduct of the sister or brother.
Not so with love.

Love keeps on loving no matter the other person's
fault. Love does not say, "You *mistreated me before,*"
or "*I gave in before; it's your turn,*" or "*One more time
and you're through,*" or "*This is too much,*" or "*It's not
my fault.*"

Love simply picks up wherever blame is laid and bears without *complaint, accusation,* or *grumbling.*

Surely the Apostle Paul's greatest inspiration must have come from his memory of the Damascus road incident. Whenever his mind entertained visions of Calvary, it was there that the cross-bearing actualized and the Bearer bore humanity's sins.

Agape love believes all things. This is not to say that love is naive or that love believes anything anyone tells her or all she hears. It means rather that love is always ready to *believe the best about another.* It means that out of a heart of tenderness and good will, love anticipates only good.

Love expects the best and is, therefore, willing to let down in order to fulfill its role of trust. Love doesn't give up on anyone until that person demands to be left alone. Even then, love does *not give up without a struggle.* It continues to believe all things — even that those who insist on being free to be lost will be saved. Love believes that if a person is not yet what he should be and can become, it goes even further to believe that the person will.

The best comes forth from people when they know they are believed in. Many a person has *despaired, given up* and *failed* because there was no belief in them. Love recognizes that belief is the stuff of which courage is made. Love takes the position then that if someone is empowered with belief, both in himself and from others, courage may be generated, sufficient to spur the person on to higher heights.

To believe only in the good of someone is to deny his humanity. Worse, it is an attempt to deceive the person. To be honest, sincere and helpful are to accept the person for what he is — *faults, shortcomings* and *weaknesses* — with a view toward improvement. Let there be acknowledgement (confession) and acceptance (belief) in the undesirable traits also since they are realities. It is upon these that strength, character and success may be built.

To believe all things is to believe in the person and to believe that all things are possible to him who believes in God Himself.

Love hopes all things. To pray for one another is to strengthen the person being prayed for, regardless of the outcome, the situation, or the answer to the prayer.

In response to prayer, the person is encouraged by the affirmation of God. Or, if God says "no" to the prayer, "not now," "wait a while," through prayer the person prayed for is accorded the strength of faith to continue in the will of God.

The other great strength is *hope.* Hope is the twin sister of faith. The role of the sisters has assisted pilgrims in life's journey on the highway of life. While faith is the substance of things hoped for, hope is the wish of the faithful motivated by the heartbeat of love. Love then hopes and believes. It hopes for the best in the midst of the worst. It hopes when all the forces of gloom and doom say, *"There is no hope."*

To hope is to expect, and to expect is to challenge. Some people have been spurred to noble achievements, primarily because they were aware that someone who loved them was hoping, expecting, counting on them to come through.

Hope exercises herself at two particular points:

1. *When she can't do anything about the matter.*

Whenever the object of one's affection goes astray, loses faith, or yields to the lower instincts, the concerned person may not be able to reach the other through counsel. At this point, the concerned person resorts to hoping that all will work out well.

2. *When she can't afford to do anything about the matter.*

This is perhaps the most agonizing, heartbreaking and soul-searching predicament of all — to see the mistake, to know the need, to know that you have the ability to serve the need, yet because of moral implications, you cannot afford to help.

This is where love sits in the grandstand of morality overlooking the game of life. Love wants to see everyone do well. It carries the burden of everyone upon its heart. It has the power *to help, to hold* and *to heal,* but must wait to be invited, to be officially permitted to be a party to the situation.

> "Behold, I stand at the door, and knock: if any man hear my voice, and open the door, I will come in to him, and will sup with him, and he with me."
> **Revelation 3:20**

Until the invitation is given, the hands of love, in essence, are tied. Love is never left weaponless. If it cannot afford to aid, it will hope to the point of expectation.

Agape love *"endureth all things."* When you bear all things, believe only the best and hope the best, it equips you for the supreme test of endurance. Love has thus qualified. It has borne, believed and hoped only the best. It is now ready to go the entire journey, to any and all lengths to sustain and support.

What is the use in getting *involved, bearing reproach, resentment* and *rejection* if you are going to give up later? What benefit is there in fully believing in, trusting and expecting if you are going to lose courage at the *"swelling of the Jordan"*? What profit is there in riding on the high winds of hope in all things if you are going to give up the race at the first sign of *atmospheric resistance?* Life calls for a holding on, a *dedicated determination, a stick-to-a-tiveness. Love is ready.* It will not let you down, it will not deceive and it will not let go.

Most of us have heard the expression, "He ain't heavy; he's my brother." This kind of caring makes a difference. If we care, it makes the load lighter and increases our *endurance quotient* when we are winded in the struggle of life. Love gives new energy and revives our strength.

We are made of the stuff that *tires, faints, becomes discouraged, falters, fails* and *gives up.* Life is too important. Its destiny too urgent to have a supporter, the agent on whom you depend, give up the fight at a point of difficulty. Love guarantees that this will not happen.

Love endures all things. I choose this brand of love to the end that my present life is secured, and my future good life is assured!

Love Never Ends

It is a sobering thought to observe that everything around you is in transition. Everything you see, touch and feel is fleeting. People are passing from this life to the next. What is permanent? What is substantial? What is lasting? *Love,* the only qualified respondent, answers boldly and quickly, *"I am!"*

Only the eternal can speak authoritatively about eternity. Only an eternal entity can promise never-ending services. Paul labored on love's attributes, offerings and services. Then he set about assuring the wisdom of forming an ongoing relationship with love. He did this by announcing the crowning characteristic of love: *never-ending.*

Just as love *never doubts, never gives up, never lets go, never leaves, never tires, never loses faith or hope,* it also promises to *never fail.* This eternal nature of love makes it all the more inviting.

When worlds are ending
And strongholds fail,
On the eternal love I am depending
When my soul sets sail!

This is resounding assurance. *Love never fails.* Marriages, into which one invests all of self, sometimes fail, leaving an abyss, a hurt, a loneliness, an aloneness that defies explanation. Friendships, seemingly so genuine, solid and lasting, sometimes cease or fail over some little word or deed that should not have mattered.

Older persons are sometimes *disappointed, despised* and *deserted* by children on whom they have depended. Left alone in a cold, uncaring and unfriendly world, many are devastated and permanently affected. That will never happen with love.

Love will be there. Love will continue. Love will not cease or fail!

Love Contrasted With Prophecy

To be sure, Paul does not intend to minimize, belittle, or diminish the value of prophecy. Such a gift is, without question, an enviable possession, so it should never be taken lightly. This declaration is not meant as a strike against the worth and veracity of prophecy. It is more a comparison with the emphasis again on love.

Prophecy is a wonder within itself. It makes schoolmates of the present and the future. It makes bedfellows of the what is, the what shall be, the now and the then. It foretells or gives insight into that which is to come. Prophecy, however and unfortunately, depends on time and temporalities for its existence and operation. When there is no more action of humanity, no more pleasure in the present nor fantasizing of the future, prophecy will have no place. Its voice will not only close, but its work will be done.

> **When prophecy is done,**
> **In times extreme.**
> **Around heaven's horn,**
> **Love reigns supreme.**

Love Contrasted With Language

Paul reminds the Corinthians, who placed high value on tongues, that the time would come when tongues would cease. He points out that this is what love has above and beyond prophecy. As with tongues, so with all languages, they shall cease.

The obvious difference between prophecy and love can be seen in the fact that languages are not always known or understood by all, but love speaks a *universal language!* When all forms and types of communication are terminated, the language of love will be ongoing.

There is an old saying, "I would rather see a sermon than hear one." There seems to be an analogy to the soul's attitude toward love and prophecy.

Imagination has the soul say, ''I would rather have the action of love than the words of tongues or languages.'' Love answers, ''You have it, for even though there are tongues (languages), they shall cease or be silenced, but I (love) will go on and on!''

Love Contrasted With Knowledge

''**For we know in part...**'' (1 Corinthians 13:9). The perfect choice of words for this declaration is, ''Let no one boast of knowledge.''

Knowledge is fleeting. It is like the will-o-the-wisp. Just when you think it is in hand, it vanishes into nothingness. What we knew or thought we knew yesterday, is changed or improved on today, so the knowledge of yesterday is gone. What we know today is already being affected by tomorrow.

Call it senility or whatever you wish, the fact remains that with the help of time, decay and the degenerative process, humanity comes finally to that point when the physical is too busy with its own plight. The emotional becomes disinterested. The spiritual is interested in higher things. To further assist the mental and its allies — alertness, memory and retentivity — knowledge slowly abandons until cessation sets in.

From affirmation that the world was round to the belief that the atom was the smallest division of matter, with thousands of instances in between, discovery has been made that knowledge has simply *flown* when it was thought that it had been *fulfilled!* Knowledge is close kin to time. It is to be divided into three stages: past, present and future. As surely as it is fascinating, it is also fleeting.

If then there is to be a permanency for humanity, some *unchanging, unceasing assurance* against the *uncertainties* of the powers of *debilitation* and *destruction*, it has to be something *other than, greater than* and more *stable than knowledge.*

First Corinthians 13:13 says, **"And now abideth faith, hope, charity [love], these three; but the greatest of these is charity."**

Interesting and fittingly, I shift from the *promises of prophecy,* the *entanglement of tongues* and the *kingdom of knowledge,* for all these have their moorings in three cities of eternality. These three stand head and shoulders above all others.

Faith, Hope and Love Will Yet Speak

When agents of the universe and others are silent, faith, hope and love will yet speak through the ages.

Faith

"Now faith is the substance of things hoped for, the evidence of things not seen" (Hebrews 11:1).

This covers all worlds, seasons and times. It further covers all of the needs of *all* people. Faith is what is used to move mountains, to walk on water and to pluck up trees.

It is through the faith of our fathers that we gain courage and inspiration for the liabilities of life's journey — that of Abraham going where he knew not; that of Noah preparing an ark to save his family; that of Jacob who blessed the sons of Joseph at his death; that of Moses refusing the luxuries and securities in Egypt, choosing rather to suffer affliction with the people of God; and all those other saints....

"Who through faith subdued kingdoms, wrought righteousness, obtained promises, stopped the mouths of lions,

"Quenched the violence of fire, escaped the edge of the sword, out of weakness were made strong, waxed valiant in fight, turned to flight the armies of the aliens."

Hebrews 11:33,34

Yet, faith is not the last word!

Hope

Hope is what a person uses when it seems there is no other help available. It has no hands or feet. It doesn't move mountains, walk on water, or pluck up trees. Yet, it works!

There are times, seasons and conditions when the need is not for *mountain-moving equipment, water-walking shoes,* or *tree-plucking caterpillars,* but just a *still small voice,* an inner reassurance, an attachment to the greatest Source of strength — God Himself.

Hope, though a phenomenal power within itself, is nevertheless handicapped, for obviously it must have support and cooperation from other sources in order to function at its best.

Portions of faith, belief, patience, endurance and love are ingredients which must be mixed into the recipe of hope. Yet, hope waxes well, holds her own and perseveres against the perils of life and existence.

If faith is the substance of things hoped for, the evidence of things not seen, then hope must, among other things, be the substance of things in which we have faith, the assurance of things unveiled. Hope is all this and more. It is what leads us into that which is more. Yet, hope is *not* the last word!

Love

"...but the greatest of these is charity [love]**"**
(1 Corinthians 13:13).

Greatness is the order of the eternal day. "These three" implies more than mere words. The implication may be that all things are contained in faith and hope. Faith and hope are strong, but they aren't omnipotent. They are wise, but not omniscient. They are everywhere, but not omnipresent.

There are great things in the earth all about us. The birth of a baby. A baby's cry. The pathlessness of wind. The song of birds. The howl of a jackal. The restricted path of the sun. The moon's pull on the tide. The tender heat of the distant sun. But there are other things — events, sights, joys, experiences and wonders — which will pale these into nothingness.

There is a Great beyond the greatest, a Star which shines for stars, a Sun which shines for suns, a Wonder of wonders!

Love is the first and the last word! Love is God, because God is love.

This chapter represents the greatest benefit of all for older people, and it points up *resources, rewards* and *reassurance* that come to those who trust in, commit to and rely on the Lord.

For older persons particularly, life at times becomes burdensome and threatening. God's *promises, parallels* and *powers* offer immeasurable and undefeatable assistance and support.

Older persons, then, should take heart and embrace the three great friends — faith, hope and love — ever remembering that each is great, but the greatest of them all is *love* (GOD)!

* * *

Poem
"Who Is My Brother?"
By Rev. Andrew D. Phillips

Who is my brother?
    Is he my father's other son,
Who shares with me the home?
    Or the man I meet at the end of the day,
When work at the mill is done?

Is he the man who works with me,
    Identical to my color and creed?
Or is he "just any man"
    Whom I might find in need?

Just who is my brother?
    Is he the man who sees as I see,
Who goes to church with me on Sunday?
    Or is he the man across the street,
Who works with me on Monday?

Is he the man who is able most,
    To help me on the way?
Or may he be some pilgrim whom
    I can help day by day?

Who is my brother?
    Is he the man who thinks as I do?
Who sees life in the same bright hue?
    Or is he the man with a different
    thought,
With a right to think his thoughts, too?

Yes, these are my brothers,
    God in heaven, Father of all mankind,
Before whom we should have none other,
    Every human creature of His divine hand
IS MY BROTHER!

APPENDIXES

Included in the Appendixes you will find "Rules for Peaceful Living" and "Don'ts for Wholesome Living" to help you in your graceful walk with the Lord in these, your latter and most blessed years.

My personal prayer for you is that your latter end will be even more blessed than your beginning (Job 42:12).

Rev. Andrew D. Phillips

Appendix 1
Rules for Peaceful Living

1.   Don't try to keep up. Let the world catch up to you.

2.   Get plenty of rest. Your body needs it.

3.   Don't travel wearing suspenders. They will pull on you and tire you.

4.   Don't try to keep up. Live at your own pace.

5.   Don't worry. Things usually turn out alright.

6.   Keep exercising.

7.   Eat lightly.

8.   Don't try to do what you used to. It's unnecessary and probably impossible.

9.   Keep a song in your heart and a smile on your face.

10.   Think beautiful thoughts of people and things.

11   Believe in, see and search for the good and the beautiful in all people and things.

12.   Don't worry about people who mistreat you. They do themselves more harm.

13.   Know God's will for your life, and be on speaking terms with Him!

14. Don't try to drive when you are no longer a safe driver.

15. Don't allow another to control your emotions: anger, hate, love, etc.

16. Learn to enjoy your own company. You will spend lots of time alone.

17. Know God well in your own way, and strive to please Him.

Appendix 2
Don'ts for Wholesome Living

1. Don't worry. It doesn't help.

2. Don't hold anger. Anger hurts only the holder.

3. Don't let things get under your skin. There isn't room there!

4. Don't be irritable or you will irritate others.

5. Don't seek revenge. The moral law takes care of all.

6. Don't exert too much too quickly. Your time may exceed your energy.

7. Don't neglect the spiritual values. They are the only lasting ones.

8. Don't overeat. There will be other meals!

9. Don't hesitate to forgive. You will need it sometime.

10. Don't worry, even if you think it does help. You can get the same results concentrating.

11. Don't hurt other people. It doesn't help you.

12. Don't think you are the only person who is right. You might be the only one who is wrong!

13. Don't be afraid to look at what someone else sees. You might like the sight.

14.   Don't be afraid to look at yourself. You might be surprised at what you see.

15.   Don't pray only for the sins of others. This is self-discrimination.

16.   Don't live to yourself. There will come a time when you will need others to live with you.

17.   Don't shut others out, for in doing so, you shut yourself in.

18.   Don't pass up a need. You might be the next person in need.

19.   Don't ignore a need, for that need may become yours.

20.   Don't take life lightly, or it will respond in kind.

21.   Don't expect more than you give. The Source will not accommodate.

22.   Don't expect more than you give. This is against the moral law.

23.   Don't forget to help others. Therein lies your help.

24.   Don't forget to bless others, or blessings may forget you!

25.   Don't wonder if right wins. Just know that wrong doesn't!

26.   Don't fight with an adversary. Win over him!

27.   Don't look down. There's more to see above.

28.   Don't piddle in the dirt when there are stars to be hung.

29. Don't fuss about fiddles when the band is already playing.

30. Don't settle for hash when the steak of opportunity is available.

31. Don't let anyone spoil your day. Make it yourself!

32. Don't try to graduate from life. It will put you back in first grade.

33. Don't pamper yourself. You are *not* a baby!

34. Don't overrate yourself. You will be alone in the process.

35. Don't be too religious. That's not good religion.

36. Don't think you are special with God unless He is special with you.

37. Don't let your head get too big from anything other than natural head growth!

38. Don't brag - you had help.

39. Don't procrastinate, the clock is still running.

40. Don't do wrong. Right will judge.

41. Don't fuss about the view. Raise your sights.

42. Don't destroy the building of society. You live in it.

43. Don't encourage hate. It breeds itself.

44. Don't teach your children to hate, or they will be the victims of it.

45. Don't hate. Hate begets hate.

46. Don't ignore God. He might confirm it.

47. Don't play with death. It plays for keeps.

48. Don't criticize the view. Clean it up.

49. Don't oil the wheel of hate. It runs well on its own.

50. Don't hold a grudge. You might be the only one with it!

About the Author

Rev. Andrew D. Phillips

The Rev. Andrew D. Phillips was born in Morris County, Texas, where he attended elementary and high school. Under the guidance of Christian parents, he joined the First Baptist Church where his knowledge and love for God grew to such a proportion that, as a youth, he became extremely active in the church.

Rev. Phillips studied at Bishop College in Marshall, Texas, where he received Bachelor of Arts and Master of Education Degrees. He completed seminary studies at Perkins School of Theology, Dallas, Texas. For 2 1/2 years, he served as an instructor of an adult education program and as principal of the Emmitt C. Scott High School, Sommerville, Texas.

Rev. Phillips answered the call of the colors in World War II and served his country for 3 1/2 years. In 1946, he heeded a higher and more urgent call — a call to ministry — and he has been a proclaimer of the Good News of Jesus Christ ever since.

The author's wide range of experiences and search for knowledge, coupled with his deeply-rooted consecration, have afforded him rich resources for this book.

Since earlier years when Andrew sang in quartets, taught and studied in school and searched for wisdom and knowledge in seminary, he has continued to study in the "world's school of practice and preparation."

Rev. Phillips has served in the following capacities:

* He taught Field Education at Oral Roberts University, Tulsa, Oklahoma.

* He has pastored churches in Texas and Oklahoma for 45 years.

* He is the past president of Coordinating Council of North Tulsa.

* He is the past president of Greater Tulsa Interdenominational Ministerial Alliance.

* He served as counselor at Washington High School, McLain High School and Gilcrease Middle School, all of Tulsa, Oklahoma.

* He gave leadership to the idea and formation of Carver Freedom School when Carver closed in the 1960s.

Currently, Rev. Phillips is involved in the following areas of leadership:

* Moderator of Northwest Creek District Association, Tulsa, Oklahoma.

* President of Martin Luther King Commemoration Society, Tulsa, Oklahoma.

* Instructor, Homiletics, Christian Ministers' Alliance, Tulsa, Oklahoma.

* Black Belt student in Karate at Dale Apollo Cook's Karate School, Tulsa, Oklahoma.

Rev. Phillips and his wife, Bernice, have three children: Phil, 33; David, 12; and Danny, 5.

Rev. Andrew D. Phillips is pastor of The Greater Mount Rose Baptist Church, Tulsa, Oklahoma.

OTHER PUBLICATIONS
BY
REV. ANDREW D. PHILLIPS

The Right and Wrong of Ushering
The Three Dimensions of Life
A Tribute to Dr. Martin Luther King, Jr.
Oh, Lord, These People